PICASSO

AND MAN

PICASSO

CATALOGUE BY JEAN SUTHERLAND BOGGS

AND MAN

THE ART GALLERY OF TORONTO
JANUARY 11–FEBRUARY 16, 1964

THE MONTREAL MUSEUM OF FINE ARTS
FEBRUARY 28–MARCH 31, 1964

LENDERS TO THE EXHIBITION

Christabel, Lady Aberconway, *London, England*
Mr. Lee A. Ault, *New York*

Professor and Mrs. Gilbert Bagnani, *Toronto*
Mr. and Mrs. Bion A. Bowman, *Boston*
Mr. and Mrs. David E. Bright, *Beverly Hills*
Mr. Himan Brown, *New York*

Mrs. Mary Callery, *Paris*
Mr. Walter Carsen, *Thornhill, Ontario*
Mr. and Mrs. Hugh Chisholm,
Hillsborough, California
Mr. and Mrs. Ralph F. Colin, *New York*
Dr. and Mrs. John D. Constable, *Boston*
Mrs. Harold Crang, *Toronto*

Mr. and Mrs. Kirk Douglas, *Beverly Hills*

Mr. and Mrs. John David Eaton, *Toronto*

Mr. M. F. Feheley, *Toronto*
Mr. and Mrs. Leonard S. Field, *New York*

Mr. Victor W. Ganz, *New York*
Mr. and Mrs. Monroe Geller, *New York*
Mrs. Raymond Goodrich, *Navasota, Texas*

Mr. and Mrs. Henry John Heinz II, *New York*
Mr. Joseph H. Hirshhorn, *New York*

Mr. Sidney Janis, *New York*

Mr. and Mrs. Samuel M. Kootz, *New York*

Mrs. Phyllis B. Lambert, *Chicago*
Mr. William S. Lieberman, *New York*

Mrs. John A. MacAulay, *Winnipeg*
Mrs. George S. Mack, *New York*
Miss Margaret Mallory, *Santa Barbara*
Mr. and Mrs. David Meltzer, *Toronto*

Miss Katharine Ordway, *New York*

Mr. and Mrs. Lazarus Phillips, *Westmount, Quebec*
Mr. and Mrs. Joseph Pulitzer, Jr., *St. Louis*

Dr. and Mrs. Israel Rosen, *Baltimore*
Mr. Peter A. Rübel, *New York*

Mrs. Bertram Smith, *New York*
Mr. James Thrall Soby, *New Canaan, Connecticut*
Mr. G. Hamilton Southam, *Ottawa*
Mr. and Mrs. T. M. Sterling, *Toronto*
Mr. and Mrs. Donald S. Stralem, *New York*
Miss Ciannait Sweeney, *New York*

Mr. Vincent Tovell, *Toronto*

Mr. and Mrs. John W. Warrington, *Cincinnati*
Mrs. John Wintersteen, *Villanova, Pennsylvania*

Mr. and Mrs. S. J. Zacks, *Toronto*
Mr. Richard S. Zeisler, *New York*

and anonymous lenders

The Baltimore Museum of Art, *Baltimore*
The Evergreen House Foundation, *Baltimore*
The Museum of Fine Arts, *Boston*
The Brooklyn Museum, *Brooklyn*
The Albright-Knox Art Gallery, *Buffalo*
The Fogg Art Museum,
Harvard University, *Cambridge*
The Art Institute of Chicago, *Chicago*
The Cincinnati Art Museum, *Cincinnati*
The Cleveland Museum of Art, *Cleveland*
The Columbus Gallery of Fine Arts, *Columbus*
The Detroit Institute of Arts, *Detroit*
Gemeentemuseum, *The Hague*
The Wadsworth Atheneum, *Hartford, Connecticut*
The Hermitage Museum, *Leningrad*
The Los Angeles County Museum of Art, *Los Angeles*
The Currier Gallery of Art,
Manchester, New Hampshire
The Pushkin State Museum of Fine Arts, *Moscow*
The Museum of Modern Art, *New York*
The National Gallery of Canada, *Ottawa*
Musée National d'Art Moderne, *Paris*
The Pasadena Art Museum, *Pasadena*
The Philadelphia Museum of Art, *Philadelphia*
The Museum of Art,
Rhode Island School of Design, *Providence*
The Virginia Museum of Fine Arts, *Richmond*
The City Art Museum of St. Louis, *St. Louis*
Washington University, *St. Louis*
The Marion Koogler McNay Art Institute, *San Antonio*
The San Francisco Museum of Art, *San Francisco*
The Santa Barbara Museum of Art, *Santa Barbara*

Stephen Hahn Gallery, *New York*
M. Knoedler & Co., Inc., *New York*
Samuel M. Kootz Gallery, *New York*
Jerrold Morris International Gallery Limited, *Toronto*
Perls Galleries, *New York*
Picasso Arts Inc., *New York*
Galerie Rosengart, *Lucerne*
Saidenberg Gallery, Inc., *New York*

Even before he settled permanently in Paris in 1904, at the age of 23, Picasso's pre-eminence was recognized by his fellow artists who made up 'Le Bande Picasso.' In addition to his painter friends, his genius soon attracted a group of stimulating intellectuals which included outstanding poets, critics and dealers (among them Guillaume Apollinaire, Max Jacob, Daniel-Henri Kahnweiler, Jaime Sabartés, André Salmon and Gertrude Stein). Throughout all the many movements and *isms* which have marked the history of art in this century, Picasso has been the recognized master to whom all the most revolutionary advances are universally ascribed. No other artist has so profoundly affected the development of modern art.

'How can we judge what honour should be done to a man of such stature?' Roland Penrose asks in the closing pages of his book *Picasso: His Life and Work*. Many attempts have been made to answer Penrose's question in the form of exhibitions, over one hundred since the first in which he exhibited at the age of fourteen. The last major one in a museum was at the Tate Gallery, London, in 1960, which almost half-a-million people visited.

Why then should yet another Picasso exhibition be organized? Except for a small and distinguished group of paintings brought together by James Johnson Sweeney for The Art Gallery of Toronto in 1949, Canada has never had the privilege of seeing a large and comprehensive exhibition of Picasso's work. This present showing of more than two hundred and fifty paintings, sculptures, drawings and prints, covering every period of the artist's career, provides an unique opportunity for Canadians to experience at first hand the immensity of Picasso's genius.

It is our hope that the exhibition is also justified by emphasizing through its theme, *Picasso and Man,* the artist's intense humanity and passionate concern for our human condition. From his early tender and beautiful *Child Holding a Dove,* 1901, to his *Head of a Woman,* 1960, he speaks to us eloquently of the deepest aspects of human experience. His work has always subscribed to the belief that art should spring from a primitive need to express our emotional reactions to our environment. Because of this it is impossible for us to be indifferent when we are confronted with his *oeuvre.* Enraged or enchanted, we are forced to think and feel and take a stand. 'The essential in this time of moral poverty is to create enthusiasm.' So said the artist himself.

Whenever an exhibition is held, the organizers feel a great sense of obligation to the lenders. In this case our feeling is particularly acute because many of the paintings have been away from their homes so frequently before. The difficult problem of deciding who among the lenders should be mentioned first is here made easier by the immense generosity of The Museum of Modern Art, New York. Through the cooperation of its director, René d'Harnoncourt, the kindness of Alfred H. Barr, Jr., Director of Museum Collections, and William S. Lieberman, Curator of Prints and Drawings, eleven paintings, one piece of sculpture, ten drawings and many prints were borrowed from that museum alone. Their cooperation in letting us have such key works as *Les Demoiselles d'Avignon,* 1907, was crucial in making this event possible. We also very much appreciate their advice in helping us to obtain other important works in the New York area and the *Guernica* studies from the artist.

In another important loan, the four early cubist pictures from the U.S.S.R., we should like to say how moved we are by this gesture from our colleagues, the directors of the two museums in Leningrad and Moscow, and the U.S.S.R. Ministry of Culture. In the negotiations necessary to borrow these paintings, we were completely dependent upon the good will and the efforts of Arnold Smith, Canadian Ambassador to the U.S.S.R., Charles F. Comfort, Director, The National Gallery of Canada, G. H. Southam and Mary Q. Dench, Information Division, Department of External Affairs, to whom we should like to express our thanks at this time.

To all the lenders, whose names are listed on the opposite page, we can never adequately express our profound gratitude. In addition there have been many others who helped in different ways to bring the exhibition together and to interpret the material for the catalogue; among those we should particularly like to thank: Philip R. Adams, Elizabeth Baer, Richard F. Brown, Charles E. Buckley, David G. Carter, Douglas Cooper, George D. Culler, Charles C. Cunningham, Bernard Dorival, William E. Eisendrath, Jr., James Elliott, Kathleen M. Fenwick, Paul L. Grigaut, Maurice Jardot, Una E. Johnson, D.-H. Kahnweiler, Samuel M. Kootz, Edmund K. Kuehn, Myron Laskin, Thomas W. Leavitt, Sherman E. Lee, John P. Leeper, Abram Lerner, Henri Marceau, John M. Maxon, Thomas N. Maytham, Agnes Mongan, Charles Nagel, Charles Parkhurst, John Richardson, Helmut Ripperger, Robert Rosenblum, Gordon M. Smith, Richard L. Tooke, L. J. F. Wijsenbeek and Willis F. Woods.

All the members of the staff of The Art Gallery of Toronto, different though their roles may have been, have been needed to bring this exhibition into being and should be thanked for their zeal. Finally, I should like to express my gratitude for the enthusiasm, support and cooperation of Mr. Evan Turner, the Director of The Montreal Museum of Fine Arts, and of his staff in venturing upon this project with us.

WILLIAM J. WITHROW

Director
The Art Gallery of Toronto

CONTENTS

The dimensions in the catalogue are
those given by the owners of the works.
Height precedes width.

front cover: no. 121
back cover: no. 120

CROUCHING WOMAN/LA MISÉREUSE ACCROUPIE

PICASSO: THE EARLY YEARS

Jean Sutherland Boggs

In 1904 Picasso made the watercolour drawing of himself seated, moodily looking at a sleeping woman, which is called *Meditation* (no. 18). His own emaciated and hunched body is like the Blue Period figures he had been painting since 1901; even the coffee in the cup beside him is blue. His face expresses such concentration, however, that we feel a strength of will unlike the fatalism of the apathetic figures with which he had peopled his Blue Period canvases. His profile, although speculative and withdrawn, reveals a response to something beyond himself which is also rarely found in his earlier work.

What does this self-portrait of Picasso imply? It is certainly a romantic and self-conscious image. More importantly it represents that constant investigation of himself, of the nature of himself and, through himself, of the nature of man, which one can find in his works from the moment he returned to Barcelona in 1898. Picasso had done dazzling pictures as a young boy and dreary ones as an adolescent (he recently remarked to his dealer and old friend, Kahnweiler, 'Cette période de mes études à Barcelona, je la déteste. Ce que je faisais avant, était bien mieux) but in 1897 he had been on his own in Madrid where his analytical approach to painting as a sixteen-year-old is apparent in a letter published in a catalogue of the O'hana Gallery (*Picasso 1881-*, London 1960). He wrote to his friend Bas in Barcelona from Madrid:

' . . . I am not in favour of following any determined school because that only brings about a similarity among adherents.

The Museum of painters is beautiful, Velasquez is first class. Some of Greco's hands are magnificent. Murillo is not always convincing. Titian's 'Dolorosa' is good: there are some beautiful Van Dyck portraits. Rubens has snakes of fire as his prodigy.'

That stay in Madrid, an attack of scarlet fever and his convalescence from it in the isolation of Horta de San Juan (or Horta de Ebro as it is also called), a place to which he was to return much later, seems to have left him, at seventeen, an independent painter.

Señor Cirici-Pellicer, and Sir Anthony Blunt and Miss Phoebe Pool have chronicled the character and complexity of the intellectual and artistic life in Barcelona which influenced young Picasso. At the same time that he was reacting to those influences from 1898 to 1900, he was also tentatively revealing in his paintings what he could discover about the life of man. From the number of portrait drawings he made during these years in Barcelona, one would assume he was most conscious of man's individuality. But a close friend since 1898, Jaime Sabartés, tells us he drew many of them when he was challenged to hold an exhibition at the café Els 4 Gats in 1900 to rival an exhibition of portrait drawings the popular Barcelona illustrator, Ramon Casas, had held at the Salon Parés the year before 'Before long his studio was crammed with portraits . . .' Sabartés writes. 'As soon as there were enough of them, or perhaps as soon as he began to seem bored with this joke, we took them all over to Els 4 Gats.' In spite of this incident there must have been some reason Picasso responded to the challenge and had made so many portraits before 1900.

Although Sabartés describes these sitters as 'just a group of nonentities badly dressed for the most part' they seem on the contrary to be nattily attired (no. 3) or at least conscious of their clothes when they happen to be in shirt sleeves (no.1) or in a workman's smock and hat (no. 2). This seems a form of dandyism which like their disaffected manner and pale faces is part of the disillusionment of the *fin de siècle* spirit in the whole of Europe. In these portraits there is an essential human loneliness and rootlessness which Picasso also

implies in his other paintings like *The Bullfight* (no. 5) and the *Street Scene* (no. 6) of 1900.

Picasso may have suggested little willpower in his portraits of his friends up to this time but his own will was strong and drove him to Paris for a short stay in 1900 and for a longer one in 1901. 1901, which he divided pretty much between Madrid and Paris, must have been one of the most incredible years of Picasso's life; he produced so much and moved in so many different directions. More than any other period it seems to illustrate the anecdote Gertrude Stein told, 'Later one day when Picasso and I were discussing the dates of his pictures and I was saying to him that all that could not have been painted during one year Picasso answered, you forget we were young and we did a great deal in a year.' In 1901 he was twenty.

In his introduction to the exhibition at Berthe Weill's in Paris in 1902 which included some of Picasso's works from 1901, Harlor (the pseudonym for Adrien Farge) wrote of three studies of women that they were, 'dediées à la misère, à la solitude, à l'épeurement . . . L'une surtout, personnifie bien la détresse, l'isolement parmi les inhumaines consolations de la nature.' If one can come to a single conclusion about the content of those pictures, it would seem to rest in Picasso's consciousness of the poles of innocence and evil and the occasional masquerade of one behind the other. There is nothing explicitly religious about this attitude nor anything in it which cannot be found in the work of contemporary artists like Munch and Beardsley, for example. But there was an intensity with which the twenty-year-old Picasso sought out the most sordid life of cafés and brothels and painted it with such vehemence (nos. 9 to 11) or on the other hand conceived innocence so sentimentally (no.12), that suggests there is some justification for speculating that he may have been making some form of moral judgment about human depravity.

At the end of 1901 Picasso had returned to Spain, and the period which is known as the Blue Period had begun. Any suggestions of judgment is gone in these paintings which his friend, the poet Apollinaire, said were 'blue as the humid depth of an abyss, and full of pity.' Gertrude Stein wrote, 'He went back again to Spain in 1902 and the painting known as his blue period was the result of that return. The sadness of Spain and the monotony of the Spanish coloring, after the time spent in Paris, struck him forcibly upon his return there.' The Blue Period figures seem removed, as even most of Picasso's earlier figures had done, from any specific time and space and seem intended to express in their heavy, inert, unarticulated bodies the weakness of man's will against the inevitability of his fate.

But if one returns to the drawing called *Meditation* one finds some of the qualities which pulled Picasso's work from its pitying, catatonic trance. The strongest of these was, perhaps, the realization of his own will which is always moodily revealed in his self-portraits and dominates when he paints himself with someone else, as he does here. Another is a responsiveness to beauty, whether it is to light falling upon his face, or to the delicacy of a line, or to the body of the woman, which suggests a greater optimism on Picasso's part about the destiny of man. And finally there is the woman herself, earthy, relaxed and smilingly confident as she sleeps, to whom some credit must be given for the change in Picasso's work. She was, of course, his first mistress Fernande Olivier.

Not long after Picasso moved to Paris permanently in 1904 and had begun to live in the tenement nicknamed the 'Bateau Lavoir,' he met Fernande who came to live with him and stayed through what may well have been the most crucial (and least prosperous) period of his career. Before she left him during the spring of 1912 he had gone through the Rose Period, painted the *Demoiselles d'Avignon*

(no. 46) and forged well ahead into analytical cubism, certainly one of the most adventurous developments in the history of twentieth century art.

Picasso's work did not abruptly change with the move to Paris and the meeting with Fernande. Even his Rose Period works of 1905 do not have the sensuality and naturalness and analytical detachment of his watercolour drawing. They are prettier than the Blue Period works, more delicate in line and colour. Their inhabitants are more involved by destiny with other human beings, the members of their families or troups of saltimbanques. But at the same time their beauty and their very bodies seem ephemeral as if such a vision of man could not survive.

Two significant things seem to have happened in Picasso's work in 1905 and 1906. One was his awareness of the beauty of the female nude (nos. 31 and 33). For the first time he painted and drew it without that Spanish sense of guilt which seems to have troubled his earlier paintings of it (no. 8); in fact this new sense of its dignity and of its sensuality moved Picasso from the Gothic tradition into the classical and Mediterranean. He also painted and drew his nudes with an innate modesty which can remind one of late archaic Greek female figures which, however, were never nude. In 1905 and 1906 the female nude represented for Picasso, obviously but not insignificantly, an interest outside himself – but perhaps more interestingly that for a moment he conceived something in an ideal rather than an expressive way.

The second significant element in Picasso's work becomes much stronger in 1906; that is the independence of the figures in his paintings. In the great work which emerged from his summer at Gosol, the Albright-Knox's *La Toilette* (no. 33), the nude figure seems to enjoy the freedom of her body as she stretches her arms upward to knot her hair. And her companion is like a sturdy and free-standing

pillar. Both have space and air in which to move unlike the claustrophobically confined figures of the Blue Period (nos. 13 to 17). The men and women Picasso painted in 1906 have become secure and substantial and free, imagined in a classical way rather than as captives of a Gothic fate.

The very brief period of these independent and sensually beautiful, if somewhat pale, men and women of 1905 and 1906 leaves one unprepared for what many of his friends regarded as the catastrophe of 1907, the painting of the *Demoiselles d'Avignon* (no. 46) in which classical beauty is destroyed and individual human will swallowed up by some malignant destiny.

The early work of Picasso also leaves us with certain problems which the two, quite different, women who knew him best at this period have posed for us. One was Fernande who asked about the etching of *The Frugal Repast* of 1904 but might have asked it about all his work, '*Qu'y avait-il au fond de cela? L'oeuvre était-elle toute cérébrale comme je l'ai comprise depuis, ou révélait-elle un profond et désespérant amour de l'humanité comme je l'ai cru alors?*' The other was Gertrude Stein who wrote, '*The head the face the human body these are all that exist for Picasso . . . the souls of people do not interest him, that is to say for him the reality of life is in the head, the face and the body and this is for him so important, so persistent, so complete that it is not at all necessary to think of any other thing and the soul is another thing.*' These are two fundamental problems: Fernande's – the degree to which Picasso was motivated by his intellect or by love; Gertrude Stein's – whether Picasso was as indifferent as she claims to the souls of men. It is hoped that this exhibition, which is dedicated to Picasso's preoccupation with man throughout his career, will provide an answer to both.

John Golding

When Picasso settled permanently in Paris in 1904 he had to face the challenge of finding himself at the centre of the most advanced group of artists in the world. Had he remained in Spain, he might well have developed into an artist like Goya – a genius certainly, but a genius working in comparative isolation, having no immediate influence on the development of Western art. The most advanced painting being produced in Spain during the early years of the new century still had a strong *fin de siècle* flavour. In Paris, on the other hand, poets and critics were prophecying the advent of something completely new. By choosing to live there, Picasso injected the greatest and most revolutionary talent of the age into an unusually vital and experimental atmosphere. Out of this fusion the truly new art of the twentieth century was born.

Stimulated by contact and rivalry with artists such as the leader of the young, *avant-garde* Fauve group, Matisse, Picasso produced the great 'Rose' paintings of 1905. With these paintings he emerged as a major master, but as a master playing variations on traditional themes. Although there are indications that Picasso admired Fauvism for its directness and immediacy, he seems to have sensed that it was not so much the beginning of a new phase of art, as the final flowering of the Post-Impressionism of the eighties and nineties, a movement doomed to short duration by its very bouyancy and lack of discipline. Perhaps, also, still very conscious of himself as a foreigner, Picasso was too proud to join a movement in which he had played no formative part. Yet despite the serene beauty of such works of 1906 as *La Toilette* (no. 33), Picasso shared much of the Fauve painters' restlessness. While Matisse (to whom Picasso was beginning to appear as a rival) was gracefully and deliberately taking his leave of the nineteenth century and the world of the Post-Impressionists and symbolists in such works as *La Joie de Vivre* of 1905-06 (Barnes Foundation, Merion,

Pennsylvania), Picasso was haunting the galleries of the Louvre, consulting the art of the more distant past, and gathering together his resources to make a major bid for attention.

The poet André Salmon, one of Picasso's closest friends at this time, has left us an account of Picasso's state of mind. 'Picasso was unsettled. He turned his canvases to the wall and abandoned his brushes . . . during long days and nights, he drew, giving concrete expression to the images which haunted him, and reducing these images to their essentials. Seldom has a task been harder, and it was without his former youthful exuberance that Picasso started on a great canvas that was to be the first fruit of his researches.'

The 'great' canvas was, of course, the *Demoiselles d'Avignon* (no. 46). It is a daring and disturbing painting today – fifty-six years ago it must have seemed nothing short of incredible. It was a leap into the unknown, and it certainly baffled and dismayed even Picasso's warmest supporters. And the *Demoiselles* is in many ways an unsatisfactory painting with its abrupt changes of style, its violence and its suppressed eroticism (originally the composition was to have included two clothed male figures). Picasso himself considered the painting unfinished. But by posing many of the problems that the Cubists were to solve, it marks the beginning of a new era in the history of art. It remains not only the major turning point in Picasso's career, but also the most important single pictorial document that the twentieth century has yet produced.

The sources on which Picasso drew to create this remarkable work have been frequently discussed and analyzed. Without the achievement of Gauguin, for example, such a painting could never come into existence. In the angular, elongated forms and the harsh, white high-lighting there is a reflection of Picasso's interest in El Greco (the influence of El Greco is particularly marked in the preparatory

sketches [nos. 42 and 43] for the famous *Peasants with Oxen* in the Barnes Foundation). Then there is a direct reference to the facial conventions of Iberian sculpture in the heads of the two central figures. But viewing the painting as a prelude to Cubism, one's attention must be focused on the two major influences that went into the creation of the *Demoiselles*, for these were the same art forms that were to condition the whole development of the movement.

In the first place, the closest prototype for this sort of composition of naked and partially draped women is to be found in the work of Cézanne; indeed, the squatting figure in the bottom right hand corner, with its extraordinary deformations, was inspired by a figure in a small Cézanne owned by Matisse. It is true that Picasso has approached Cézanne in a spirit of anarchy, almost of aggression. And ultimately the Cézannesque features in the *Demoiselles* were overlaid by other, stronger influences. Nevertheless, it would not be inappropriate to see the picture as an 'Homage to Cézanne.' Cézanne had been an influence on contemporary painting since the beginning of the century, but it is this painting that makes Cézanne an honourary twentieth century artist, and it was in the following years that Cézanne's reputation as the greatest and most influential figure in nineteenth century art was really laid.

Perhaps even more important from the point of view of Picasso's subsequent development as a painter, is the fact that while he was working on the *Demoiselles*, he came into contact with African art. The mask-like face of the 'demoiselle' at the extreme left, and above all the savagely distorted and gashed faces of the two figures at the right, bear witness to the force with which this 'primitive' art struck Picasso. It is hard to pin down particular examples of Negro art which might have influenced him, for his figures of the following year (for example this exhibition, nos. 48 and 49) have the quality of *all* Negro sculpture. What is certainly true is that Picasso was interested in the principles of Negro art rather than in any particular manifestation of it. For here was an art that held the key to the young twentieth century painters' desire to emancipate themselves for visual appearances, in that it was an art that was simultaneously representational and anti-naturalistic. As opposed to the Western artist, the Negro sculptor tends to be interested not so much in recording the visual appearance of his subject, as in expressing his idea of it. Thus for the Negro, two circular shells or cylindrical pegs can come to represent eyes, a vertical slab of wood can become a nose, a horizontal one a mouth and so on. Or in other words, abstract, non-representational shapes or forms can be made to assume a representational role by their symbolic arrangement or placement in relationship to each other. Of all the Cubists, it was Picasso who most appreciated and understood what Negro art had to offer Western painting, and the lessons he learned from it enabled him to produce, during the following years, a new, anti-naturalistic art, that was at the same time a realistic art, dealing with the representation of the material world around him.

If Picasso approached Negro art at a deeper level than any of his contemporaries, this was because, for some time, he had been dissatisfied with the traditional Western approach to the painting of forms or objects. Here in the *Demoiselles* we have, albeit in a tentative, fumbling fashion, a new approach to the problem of representing three-dimensional volumes on a two-dimensional surface. It is in this that the painting's supreme originality lies. In the heads of the three figures in the left half of the composition, Picasso's intentions are stated in a crude, schematic way: the heads of the two central figures are seen full-face and yet have profile noses, while the head seen in profile has a

full face eye. In the squatting figure, the most important part of the painting (and the last to be painted), this sort of optical synthesis is extended to the treatment of the whole figure. It has been split or hinged down the central axis of the spine so that while the pose is basically a simple three-quarter view from the back (with the breast and thigh visible between upper leg and arm), the far leg and arm have been pulled around and up onto the picture plane, suggesting also an abnormally distended or splayed-out view from directly behind. For five hundred years, since the beginnings of the Italian Renaissance, artists had been guided by principles of scientific or mathematical perspective, whereby the artist viewed his subject from a single, stationary viewpoint. Here, it is as if Picasso had walked 180 degrees around his subject and had synthesized his impressions of it into a single image.

The break with traditional perspective was to result, in the following years, in what the Cubists called 'simultaneous' vision – the fusion of various views of a figure or an object into one coherent whole. The first step towards the total reconstruction of the grammar of painting had been taken. Its importance cannot be overestimated, nor must one ever forget the courage and heroism that the creation of the *Demoiselles* must have required.

Contemporary critics were unanimous in proclaiming Picasso as founder and leader of the Cubist movement, and only after the first world war was it recognized that another painter, Georges Braque, had played an equal part in its creation. The two artists met almost immediately after Picasso had finished work on the *Demoiselles,* and during the following years they worked together in a collaboration of unprecedented closeness. 'C'était comme si nous étions mariés,' Picasso recently remarked; and it is true that a spiritual, artistic marriage existed between the two. Neither could have accomplished a revolution of the magnitude of Cubism without the

other's help. Yet as we distance ourselves from the movement, it becomes increasingly possible to distinguish the individual contribution of each artist.

Picasso approached Cubism through an interest in solid, three-dimensional form. Of his works of the 'Negroid' period, executed during the years immediately after the *Demoiselles* (for example in this exhibition, nos. 48 and 49), Picasso once said that each figure could be easily realized in terms of free-standing sculpture; the powerful bronze *Head of a Woman* (no. 53) testifies to the fact that he conceived of Cubist form in sculptural terms. Braque's first major contribution, on the other hand, was to produce a new Cubist space to complement and surround Picasso's Cubist forms. This space was in Braque's own words a 'tactile' or 'manual' space; like Picasso's early Cubist images it was in a sense 'measurable'. By giving the empty areas between the objects the same faceted, solid treatment as the objects themselves, Braque was able to assert that space was as real, as pictorially important as the objects it surrounded. These spatial sensations, Braque realized, were implicit in the late canvases of Cézanne, just as Picasso had seen that Cézanne's mysterious distortions of form suggested a new approach of three-dimensional volumes.

Picasso was, however, perhaps too impetuous and violent a nature to come to terms immediately with the extreme subtlety and complication of Cézanne's art. Certainly he was more immediately moved and excited by his discovery of African art. There can be little doubt that, when in the latter part of 1908 and early 1909, Picasso turned again to the work of the earlier painter, it was largely through Braque's example; the renewed influence of Cézanne can be seen in works such as the magnificent *Dryad* from Russia (no. 49). The rigourous, rational analysis of forms suggested by Negro sculpture is now tempered by a more empirical, 'painterly' approach. The results of the perfect fusion of lessons learned from

Cézanne's art with the more conceptual, sculptural qualities of the 'Negroid' canvases are to be seen in Picasso's first truly Cubist canvases of 1909 and 1910, of which the *Woman in a Chair* (no. 54) and Buffalo's *Nude* (no. 55) are characteristic examples.

For some time now, critics have distinguished between two major phases in Cubist art; an early 'Analytic' phase and a subsequent 'Synthetic' phase – a distinction originally worked out in the art and writings of Juan Gris, the third of the triumvirate of great Cubist painters. But if one accepts this division, it is equally important to subdivide Picasso's Analytic Cubism into an early experimental, Negroid-Cézannesque period and a later development that might be labelled the 'classical' or 'heroic' period, This phase, so superbly represented in this exhibition by such works as *Ma Jolie* and *Man with a Pipe* (nos. 58 and 57) was characterized by a further and more decisive break with natural appearances; because many of the paintings of this period are at first sight hard to 'read', this is also referred to as the 'hermetic' phase of Cubism. This was, in fact, a moment of perfect poise and balance which lasted approximately two years, from mid-1910 until the end of 1912.

Paradoxically, this moment of calm was in many ways the most dramatic moment in twentieth century art. It may be suggested that to the historian of the future the basic pattern or rhythm of the art of this century will appear to have been the constant pull that artists have felt between a representational kind of art and a purely abstract or non-representational means of expression. Cubism was not an abstract art. Both Picasso's contemporary statements and almost all his subsequent work show that Cubism was an attempt to produce a new, anti-naturalistic but figurative, representational art. The keys or clues that Picasso introduced into his classical Cubist paintings in order to help the spectator to reconstruct the subject – easily legible details, such as locks of hair, moustaches, pipes, buttons and newspaper headings – reaffirm his realistic intentions. But Cubism had come perilously close to total abstraction; and to many young artists, such as Mondrian and Malevitch, it was the classical Cubism of Picasso and Braque that posed the problems of abstraction versus representation boldly and for the first time.

The technical innovations which accompanied this phase in Picasso's Cubism can be readily appreciated by comparing *Ma Jolie* (no. 58) with the *Woman in a Chair* (no. 54) painted two years earlier. Instead of fragmenting and analyzing the human form into its component parts, Picasso now uses the bolder, more direct method constructing a linear grid or scaffolding, suggested by the outlines of the subject, around which he builds up a complex of hinged, interacting planes, which suggest rather than define form and space. This new method of composition allowed him greater freedom in conveying the principles evolved over the preceding years. To put it crudely, plan, section and elevation of each object or part of the body could be drawn over each other and fused into a single, 'simultaneous' entity or image.

The advent of Synthetic Cubism was heralded by Picasso's invention of 'collage' in the spring of 1912, when he glued a piece of imitation chair-caning on to one of his still lifes. *Collage* can perhaps be best described as the incorporation of extraneous matter onto the picture surface; soon Picasso was making use of materials such as cloth, pieces of paper, cigarette packages, theatre programmes, newspaper clippings and so on. Perhaps it is not too fanciful to suggest that Picasso turned to these substances because he was aware that his paintings had become highly abstract in appearance and was looking for ways to reaffirm the realism of his vision. For the pieces of *collage* are fragments of matter which exist independently in the real, material world and relate the painting to it in a very concrete way. Objects and substances which we touch and handle in daily life, when incorporated into a work of art, make a bridge between our every-day existence and the artistic fact presented to us by the painter. On another level, Picasso is making a statement about the problem of illusionism in art. In many of his Synthetic Cubist works, what at first sight appear to be fragments of *collage* are in fact passages of *trompe l'oeil* or illusionistic painting, so that what Picasso is in effect saying is that no visual reality is absolute.

It was while he was working with strips of paper and other *collage* elements that Picasso became aware of the possibilities of a new method of procedure. In his first Cubist paintings he had started with a fairly naturalistic image which was then slowly analyzed and abstracted in the light of his new ideas about using a variable viewpoint. Now the process was reversed. Working with a series of abstract pictorial shapes or elements, he realized that these could be assembled together to suggest or assume a representational function. In the *Harlequin* of 1913 (no. 63), a transitional work, broad flat upright forms are marshalled together to suggest or become the figure of a man. The process is more clearly marked in the *Head of a Man* of this same year and *The Card Player* of 1913-14 (nos. 62 and 65), where the brightly coloured shapes seem to have been derived directly from the patterned strips of paper Picasso was incorporating into his contemporary *collages*. If these works are juxtaposed to any of those executed between 1908-10, the difference between an analytic and a synthetic approach is immediately obvious. One is reminded of Gris' classical distinction between the two methods of work: 'Cézanne turns a bottle into a cylinder, but I begin with a cylinder and create a particular image of a special type; I make a bottle – a particular bottle – out of a cylinder.'

These works of 1913-14 provide a vivid illustration

of the new decorative element which accompanied the reintroduction of colour into Cubist painting during the Synthetic phase. They are characterized, too, by a new feeling of humour and gaiety. And it was in his *collages* and the works most directly related to them that Picasso was able to give the full rein to what might be called the magical, rabbits-out-of-hats aspect of his talent: a piece of crumpled paper is exuberantly transformed into a student's beret; the broken slat of a chair becomes a bottle of pernod; three pieces of string laid side by side over a circular form evoke a whole guitar. But it would be wrong to accept these works only at their decorative and carefree surface value. For they involve a totally new aesthetic concept, and one which may eventually prove to have been Picasso's most important contribution to the history of the visual arts. During the preceding years he had done much to destroy traditional pictorial conventions, and now in his *collages*, constructed out of elements salvaged, so to speak, from the rubbish heap and waste-paper basket, he destroyed completely traditional distinctions between the beautiful and ugly. By doing so Picasso was using a typically Cubist medium to detach himself from a purely Cubist aesthetic; for with all its revolutionary intent, Cubism had never been out to destroy the past. And it was the Dadaists and Surrealists who were to use Picasso's Cubism of this period as the weapon with which to attack the art of the past in an attempt to wipe clean the aesthetic slate.

The first world war did much to destroy Cubism as an organized movement. But to Picasso, who had never seen himself as a member of a group, it made little immediate difference. As a citizen of a neutral country, he was able to work on uninterruptedly, and it was he, together with his compatriot Juan Gris, who kept Cubism alive during the war years. During 1914 there was a steady flow of gay, highly coloured canvases, so strikingly decorative that one critic was prompted to coin the term 'rococo' Cubism to describe them. The work of the following year, however, is very different in mood. Picasso's restlessness and his unhappiness at the sensation of world tragedy found their greatest expression in works such as the large *Harlequin* from New York's Museum of Modern Art (no. 66). The forms still derive from Picasso's experiments with *collage*, but they achieve a new monumentality and an almost architectural economy. Despite the elegance of colour, this work is tinged by an element of sadness, which reflects the fact that Picasso was now isolated from his friends, both physically and by the fact that he was now fully established financially and artistically. The days of communal bohemian existence which had left their stamp on early Cubist painting and aesthetics were over, for him, for ever.

After the war, with a few striking exceptions, Picasso's most important achievements in figure painting were realized in his new, Neo-Classical style, while Cubism tends to be reserved for his essays in still life. These reached a climax in the monumental series of still lifes before open windows executed in 1924. The decorative appeal of these works with their combination of simplicity and opulence is, however, matched by such masterpieces of figure painting as *Si Tu Veux* of 1918 and above all the two versions of the *Three Musicians* now in The Museum of Modern Art, New York, and in The Philadelphia Museum of Art, all executed during the period of Picasso's association with the Diaghilev Ballet. Picasso, who had appeared to the world successively in the guise of a socially conscious anarchist, a lyrical classicist, a revolutionary and a destroyer, now emerges with these works as a glittering virtuoso. These are still Cubist works, but they are Cubism redone in terms of the theatre and the carnival.

It is easy to say where a style begins, much harder to say where it ends. But 1925 can be taken as marking the end of the Cubist epoch. Gris died in 1927, and during his last year of illness produced relatively little. Braque's work was becoming increasingly personal. And in 1925 Picasso painted his *Three Dancers* (still in his possession, exhibited at The Art Gallery of Toronto 1949), which in its violence, and the sensation of obsessive neuroticism that it produces, carries Picasso through into Surrealism and points ahead to the great experimental American painting of the 1940s. The *Demoiselles* had lain neglected and abandoned as unfinished for almost twenty years. Early in 1925 it was taken out and photographed for the first time for publication in a Surrealist periodical. During the preceding years Picasso, in his large and very beautiful Neo-Classical Maternities, had come as close to bourgeois conformity as was possible for an artist of his temperament. It is tempting to think that when Picasso looked again at the *Demoiselles* and produced this new landmark in his art, he was reassessing the Cubist achievement and gathering up his resources for fresh endeavours. His Cubism was an art of experiment that had stood still for only one brief moment of classical poise. It had fearlessly confronted and produced a new kind of reality. It had evolved a completely original, anti-naturalistic kind of figuration, which had at the same time stripped bare the mechanics of pictorial creation, and had in the process gone a long way towards destroying artificial barriers between abstraction and representation. For twentieth century art in general this was an act of the utmost importance. And seen within the context of Picasso's own development the years between 1908 and 1913 emerge as a period of unequalled concentration which provide the basis for the understanding of all his subsequent work.

Robert Rosenblum

After the First World War, strange rumblings from that subterranean portion of the mind which Freud had called the *id* began to be felt throughout Western art and letters; and soon, an official commitment to the charting of these irrational regions was made in André Breton's first Surrealist Manifesto of 1924. Like a seismograph, Picasso's own art of the twenties quickly registered these disquieting tremors. If the great years of Cubism had concentrated on the creation of a pictorial language as radically new and relevant to our century as the invention of one-point perspective had been to the Renaissance, the ensuing years turned to an exploration of human experience that had been largely suppressed by these consuming intellectual and aesthetic endeavours. Already in 1907, the *Demoiselles d'Avignon* had exploded a volcano of savage forces that were, however, to be quickly restrained under the cerebral controls of early Cubism. Again in 1925, a new group of maenads – the *Three Dancers* – recklessly burst into a bacchanalian realm of terror and frenzy that was to reverberate more loudly throughout the next decade.

The exhibition's first major statement of this frightening new domain – one that might be called Psychoanalytical Cubism – is the *Seated Woman* of 1926-27 (no. 93), which uses a Cubist vocabulary as if seen through a distorting mirror. Jigsaw-puzzle compactness; dramatic intersections of stylized light and shadow; ambiguous elisions of ironed-out planes – all these by now familiar Cubist devices are suddenly directed toward the creation of a monster whose distortions no longer seem the by-product, but rather the very goal, of the Cubist's freedom to rearrange the human form. Within the warped network of planes that describe a wall with a red decorative moulding and the diagonal weave of a chairback, a woman in a black-striped dress is transformed into an image of ritual horror that recalls both the unsettling power of African Negro masks and the iconic stare and intensity of the Romanesque frescoes of Picasso's native Spain. Anatomy is wildly re-invented. One hand becomes a stump that echoes the wriggling lines of print in an open book; the other, a no less subhuman claw. Breasts and face are reduced to magical nodes of nipples, eyes, nostrils, ears and mouth that cut far below the decorous environment of a domestic interior that shelters a reading woman. Indeed, these inanimate trappings of civilization – chairs, clothing, books, walls – become more and more ironically opposed to the humanoid beings that move among them. As if on the psychiatrist's couch, they seem to be divested of censoring will and intellect so that we may uncover, if we dare, hidden realms of desire and sexuality, fear and sadism.

Typically for his virile biography, Picasso generally practices these pictorial psychoanalyses on women, who may be metamorphosed alternately into mysterious receptacles of tender and voluptuous procreative power or bestial creatures that, like female mantises, savagely await their sexual prey. In both cases, however, the descent from the human to the subhuman, from the conscious to sub-conscious, dominates Picasso's imagery of the late twenties and thirties, as it does that of the more orthodox Surrealists.

Some of these women are of an almost unbearable ugliness and brutality. In a head of 1928 (no. 98), Picasso lowers the human race to the very bottom of the evolutionary ladder, disclosing an amoeboid creature which parallels the squirming, unicellular organisms that pulsate throughout Miró's equally elemental world of Surrealist biology. The mouth, crudely contracted as if with toothlike stitching, provides the most primitive of orifices; two unclosing eyes add another basic biological function; and six bristles of hair might almost be antennae seen through a microscope.

Elsewhere, this biomorphic vocabulary, whose undulant, protoplasmic shapes are so foreign to the cerebral geometries of early Cubism, can change to a spiky aggressiveness, as of some carapaced reptile. Occasionally – witness the *Head of a Man* of 1913 (no. 62) – the fracturings of Cubism could produce a whimsically grotesque face, but in the late twenties, these sharp planes and acute angles become truly menacing. In one figure of 1929 (no. 102), which brilliantly asserts the Spanish colour scheme of red, yellow, and black so recurrent in Picasso's and Miró's work, the breasts and nose are as pointed as armour and the tongue becomes a barb that darts across a mirror frame from behind a row of subhuman teeth. Two creatures of the same prehistoric race are found in *Heads,* also of 1929 (no. 103). All the more disarming because of the prim striped dressed and tidy beaded collars, these scarecrows, with tongues like swordtips and skin like a shield, confront each other in a mirrorlike colloquy whose impact is at once comical and hideous. And in *Woman in an Armchair* of 1929 (no. 104), this most Spanish equation for the grotesque is maintained. If one is amused by the leisurely abandon of this white-frocked monster who relaxes in an armchair upholstered with purple and yellow stripes, one is no less horrified by her anatomy. A pinpointed head with beady eyes and insectlike mouth; fatty, sunburned limbs and breasts that burst from a tightly corseted robe – these transform her into an ancestor of the less equivocal horror of deKooning's *Woman* of the early fifties.

In the late twenties and thirties, this fathoming of concealed, irrational forces is reflected, too, in Picasso's attachment to the theme of the artist in his studio and, more particularly, the very act of translating nature into art. In Cubism, this interplay between the worlds of art and reality had also dominated Picasso's new objectifications of the components of pictorial illusion and, even more, his witty shufflings of true and false in the collages; but these concerns pertained more to a domain of intellectual and formalist investigation. Now, the artistic process becomes something magical and incomprehensible, as if Picasso were trying to seek out the ritualistic mysteries associated with the dawn of art. Sometimes, these quiet and intense confrontations between artist and subject occur within the calm, Arcadian environment of his Neoclassic style, as in the ravishing outline etchings of 1933, *The Sculptor's Studio*. But elsewhere – in one of the last plates of this series (May 4, 1933) and in the 1934 etching that balances a ferociously hirsute and leonine Rembrandt against a nude of classical tranquility – this relation between artist and model can become a bizarre dialectic between the ideal and the grotesque. Similarly, in the *Harlequin* of 1927 (no. 92), Picasso takes one of his favourite motifs, transforms it into a monster of gaping parrot eyes and sphincteral mouth ringed with teeth, and then, by setting it into a picture-within-a-picture and casting across it a magically luminous classical profile that is distortedly reflected in the flowing contours of the harlequin, evokes the mysteries of the artist's ability to create both transcendent beauty and ugliness.

Although Picasso himself would disclaim his allegiance to orthodox Surrealism in anything but such composite furniture-figures as seen in some of the Daliesque drawings of the summer, 1933 (no. 147), it might nevertheless be argued that his masterpieces of the early thirties are, in fact, the greatest triumph of the Surrealists' efforts to create a pictorial style and imagery appropriate to the exploration of dreams, and to the uncovering of those profound biological roots that link man more firmly to irrational nature than to a technological civilization. To do this, Picasso invented a language of multiple metaphors far more evocative and poetic than the more literal-minded *trompe-l'oeil* double-images

and fantastic figures of many of the Surrealists who attempted to unchain the subconscious. The capital year of this achievement was 1932, when Picasso was living in relative seclusion at the Château de Boisgeloup with a woman, Marie-Thérèse Walter, whose drowsy, bovine nature is constantly reflected in the work of the early thirties. Again and again, Picasso would seize various moods of repose in his painting, ranging from catnaps and daydreams to the most profound slumber, and would miraculously find visual equivalents to describe this progressive dissolution of consciousness.

In two of the works exhibited, the grey reverie of the sibylline *Seated Woman* of summer, 1932 (no. 108) moves further and further inward to unveil the erotic mysteries of deep sleep. With the *Nude on a Black Couch* of March 9, 1932 (no. 109) and *Reclining Nude* of July, 1932 (no. 110) – two paintings that bracket chronologically the pictorial and poetic summit of these meditations, the *Girl Before a Mirror* – Picasso's genius is at its height. The earlier work may be profitably compared with the *Sleeping Peasants* of 1919 (no. 72) in order to perceive the shift in Picasso's art from the description of physical to psychological realities, for the position of the sleeping woman is almost identical in these two pictures. In the former, Picasso grasps the qualities of coarse, peasant torpor – a noonday siesta under a scorching sun that turns the giant figure into a sodden, earthbound weight. In the 1932 image of sleep, the release occurs in a subconscious realm; for the body now seems deprived of material substance, while nevertheless retaining the rounded fullness of female fertility. This descent below consciousness is achieved by pictorial puns which may depend ultimately on the visual *double-entendres* of Cubism, but which exist here in an anti-intellectual realm of erotic magic that stands as one of the highpoints of Surrealist poetry. Thus, night, love, and procreation are suggested by the

hair, which also becomes a kind of seed that just touches an ovarian breast; by the green stem and white flower that grow from a hand relaxed in sleep; by the crescent-moon shape of a closed eye; or by the philodendrons that, newly nurtured by the orange-red heat of dawn just visible through the window, rise from the protective, uterine folds of black couch and lavender flesh.

The same voluptuous surrender to sleep may be seen in the later *Reclining Nude* (no. 110). Here again, the body is steeped with shades of lavender and purple, nocturnal colours that, in the thirties, often convey for Picasso a growing intensity of sleep and inwardness that would vanish under the physical light of day. Slumbering on a green meadow alive with white flowers, the nude once more becomes a vessel of fertility in harmony with nature. In a characteristically Surrealist metaphor, her blond hair can be read simultaneously as leaf, seed, and vulva; and the burgeoning plants that sprout in the background stem from human thighs that, like fresh tendrils, are outlined in green. Bones, joints, even fingers and toes are absorbed into this sensual convolution of swelling, germinal flesh. In such figures, Picasso offers among the most brilliant realizations of the Surrealist vocabulary of organic, throbbing shapes that animated so much sculpture and painting of the late twenties and thirties, witness Arp and Moore, Miro and Dalí.

With his customary refusal to relax into a single style or mood, Picasso, during the same productive summer of 1932, painted the *Bather with a Ball* (no. 111), which abruptly contradicts not only the hushed stillness of these sleeping fertility goddesses but also their adherence to a language of immaterial flatness. The beach had been a recurrent setting in Picasso's work, evoking in his earliest years a kind of social wasteland, to which his beggars and circus figures were exiled; in his Neoclassic mode, a pagan idyll of Mediterranean calm and freedom; and now, in his Surrealist years, a natural environment that permitted a maximum of animal liberty to the human species. Figures swimming and cavorting on the sand were a common theme in the twenties, but this playful mood could sometimes turn into a kind of grotesquerie familiar to the beach scenes of Miró and Dalí, where the water's edge often becomes a metaphor of the fringe of consciousness. In this painting, a prosaic beachside activity – a bather chasing a beachball – is transformed into a monstrous spectacle that, like Miró's *Figure Throwing a Stone at a Bird,* can be read as hilariously comic or terrifyingly ugly. To describe this ludicrous scene, Picasso has invented astonishing puns. The bather herself – all rounded buttocks, breasts, and limbs – is made of a grey, peumatic substances, like the inflated rubber she pursues; whereas the beachball has lost a dimension and will thus always elude her clumsy, fingerless grasp. This spherical anatomy, at first just a parody of a summer commonplace, takes on a truly Surrealist flavour in the treatment of head and hair. Recalling the invertebrate, submarine beings of Miró, this lady, appropriately enough to the seaside atmosphere, is part squid – her face, a gummy bulb; her mouth, a vertical air vent; her hair, the sea-swept tentacles that jet-propel the creature sideways and forward in pursuit of its prey. And if formal considerations may be raised in so unsettling an image of humanity, it should be added that Picasso offers, too, a dazzling interplay of two and three dimensions, so that ultimately, as in a Cubist painting, this swollen figure is tautly compressed into a flattened seascape whose deepest plane, marked by the tiny French flag, appears simultaneously to be located on the picture surface. Similarly, the *Plaster Bust and Compote* of 1933 (no. 112) juggles the continuous flatness of the background and linear still life against the vigorous spatial implications of a cubic statue base and the writhing, pendulous curves of a weirdly animate plaster head.

In the mid-thirties, Picasso's pictorial activity slackened somewhat, at least by comparison with his usual protean standards, and the works of these years often yield a cloistered silence that provides a quiet coda to the great introspective images of 1932. *Two Girls Reading* of 1934 (no. 149) and *The Poet's Attic* of 1936 (no. 164) bear out this meditative mood, in which figures, in strangely illuminated rooms, contemplate books or slumber at a writing table. In the latter work, odd prophecies of *Guernica* may be seen, not only in the grisaille palette, with its bleak network of light and shadow, but in the overhead lamp and distorted interior perspective. It was, indeed, the ominous calm before the storm. When German planes bombed the Basque capital of Guernica late in the afternoon of Monday, April 26, 1937, Picasso had already protested the Spanish regime in his *Dream and Lie of Franco,* whose sadistic monsters and convulsive agonies were also reflected in the Spanish Civil War paintings of his compatriots Miró and Dalí. But this esoteric fantasy of words and images was swiftly converted to the public statement of *Guernica,* which recorded, like the flashbulb of a news photographer, the unspeakable realities of the mid-twentieth century world. More than a century earlier, another Spanish artist, Goya, had likewise alternated between the blackest nightmares of a witches' world and the blackest reportorial facts of a war-torn Spain. Thus, in *Guernica* and in the frenetic studies that precede and follow it, the most unbelievable of Picasso's Surrealist inventions are instantly changed into the documentary truth of women's faces hideously knotted with pain, savagely pierced with tears. That one can so quickly bridge the gap between these pathetic creatures, reduced to animal suffering, and the monsters of the Surrealist years is not only a testimony to the tragedy of our own century, but to Picasso's relentless inquiry into the nature of modern man.

Evan H. Turner

Characteristically, in terms of his recent working habits, Pablo Picasso began on August 10, 1959, to explore the bucolic theme of two young men picnicing with their charming companions, a theme derived from Edouard Manet who had in turn been influenced, in creating his great 'Déjeuner sur l'Herbe,' by Giorgione. By December 29, 1961, when he signed the final composition in this series of studies, Picasso had painted and drawn 165 subjects (of which 27 were oil paintings) inspired by, and often related to, Manet's great work.

The attitude evident in these pictures exemplifies Picasso's relations with his work during the past decade. An understanding resulting from years of pictorial exploration as well as a remarkable technical facility, which permits him to express rapidly any idea that may cross his mind, have removed those restraints that are so often experienced at one time or another by all but the very greatest masters. The speed of conception and the darting imagination of exploration mean that the succession of works are virtually free associations circling around the central idyllic theme. The constantly shifting personalities of the figures, even the variations in their age, as well as the complexities resulting from the changing relationships, assure each picture's being an independent achievement, which at the same time furthers the artists's exploration of the theme as a whole. Rarely does such technical facility so thoroughly complement a breadth of human understanding and experience. A magnificent human statement such as Picasso's *Déjeuner* series is typical of his recent work.

Picasso now enjoys to the full a rare freedom. He is in an almost unique situation in the history of art. In the years since 1945 he has been internationally recognized as the great man among the painters of today; he can gain no more recognition. Whereas in his youth Picasso was a leader among his contemporaries, he is, today, in an age of essentially non-representational art, completely independent with no followers as such. He has no pressure whatsoever from patrons giving commissions; he did the *War* and *Peace* in the chapel at Vallauris and, later, the great UNESCO mural because he wanted to. He enjoys unlimited financial affluence, although after his essential needs are satisfied this seems of no greater importance to him than did the poverty of his youth.

Since Picasso is as free as a man can be, one of the most interesting factors in exploring his work of the last twenty years is to see what he has achieved with this freedom. The results are remarkable. He stays in place and he works with an intensity and a productivity matched by very few artists in the history of European painting. The results may vary at times in their degree of quality or success of realization – Picasso has observed that 'There is no such thing as a bad Picasso; some are less good than others' – but always his fundamental grandeur of attitude is apparent. The reaction of the public to his work is of little, if any, concern to him; he paints for himself, since there are so many ideas that he is compelled to consider or express. Yet, as evidenced in his paintings, the depth of his understanding for and curiosity about humanity knows absolutely no limitations.

While Picasso's humanitarian sympathies were repeatedly evident in his pre-Cubist pictures, this note was to a degree undermined in these works, at least in retrospect, by a decided element of sentimentality. For many, Picasso's most splendid statement of human sympathy was his next great social statement coming years after these pre-Cubist pictures, the anguished painting inspired by his emotions of shock and grief over the needless fascist bombing of the small Spanish market village of Guernica on April 26, 1937. This horrible event acted on him as a violent catalyst since in less than two months he painted *Guernica,* which is perhaps the most significant painting of our century to date.

Thus, even before the European war broke out, Picasso was already deeply involved emotionally with the horror of cruel and needless destruction. It is significant in the growth of his spiritual stature that whereas during the First War he continued paths of exploration inaugurated before the war broke out, as well as creating the great classic pictures which were in such contrast to the upheaval of Europe, the works painted during the 1939-1945 War are dominated by the chaos and destruction of traditional values that surrounded him in fallen France. Symbolic of Picasso's attitude in late 1942 is the essentially monochromatic nude set in a dull prison-like atmosphere (no. 234), escaping the cruel reality of the world through sleep even as her distorted body expresses its chaotic state. In a series of 'portraits' inspired by the beauty of Dora Maar, every extreme of emotional attitude was explored (nos. 229 and 230). In some of the heads he painted so often in these years a metamorphosis occurred through the introduction of animal features, notably those of his beloved Afghan hound Kasbec (no. 231).

Yet, the war years were fertile ones insofar as the evolution of his style was concerned. Perhaps reflecting the austerity of the moment, the increasing reduction in his work of the painted facts to their absolute minimum adds significantly to the force of his compositions. Because of his skillful use of drawing to suggest several different contours at once, a powerful sense of form is insistently stated even as he eliminates much of the local modelling. The stark nature characteristic of many of the late-war pictures is evident in the 1944 painting (no. 238). The care with which he understood a figure before achieving such a striking statement of its essential details can be seen in the drawings related to the kneeling figure (nos. 236 and 237). The allegorical implication that may subconsciously be implied in this picture is suggested in the last lines of Picasso's

1941 play *Desire Caught by the Tail*: '*Light the lanterns. Throw flights of doves with all our strength against the bullets and lock securely the houses demolished by bombs.*' Only in 1945 did Picasso specifically deal with the war, in *Aux Espagnols morts pour la France*, and in the *The Charnel House*, in which horror is stressed, in contrast to the violence of *Guernica*, through the absolute calm of the dead.

That the end of the war freed Picasso's spirit is quickly evident in his works. Perhaps no other work has ever suggested so movingly the bliss of peace as the great *Joie de Vivre* painted in the Musée Picasso at Antibes late in 1946. The centaur, the nymphs, the rollicking goats, the Pan and most of all the bright clear colours dominating this work are repeatedly found in the works of the next years (nos. 242-243). Probably never had Picasso so splendidly suggested the classic Mediterranean spirit as he did in these 1946 decorations in the Musée Picasso.

That element in the Spanish character which creates the depth of their religious passion explains Picasso's fervour in dealing with themes of war and peace as no French painter ever has.

It is virtually impossible to analyze methodically Picasso's development in the years since the end of the war. This strange situation occurs because a considerable portion of this production is withheld by Picasso. While many, if not all, of the major works are probably known, the analysis of these works in terms of the often more personal ones that are held back is essential in order to follow consistently the evolution of the conflicting factors that seem fundamental to Picasso's character at any one moment. However, although the artist does not choose to release all of his work, he does emphasize his current habit of concentrating upon a single motif by releasing from time to time all of his studies related to a particular theme. (This working method seems quite different from that of the pre-war years when the principal unity among a group of pictures tended to depend upon a common stylistic treatment.) In 1953, for example, a group of 180 drawings dealing with the artist and his model were published, while early in 1957 he exhibited as a group the paintings he did of his studio in the villa, La Californie. Thus, although his total evolution cannot be easily established, one can follow and analyze the pictorial synthesis of certain works as has never before been possible.

One wonders whether this method of releasing everything connected with a few works may not be motivated in part by Picasso's heightened appreciation, given his age, of every moment of creation. Whether this is so or not, it is providential that at least the loss of early material that occurred because of changes of location and the necessity to re-use material because of the artist's poverty, does not occur today.

The confusion of hopes which has characterized the Western World in the years since the war has had its effect upon Picasso. In four great works, the 1951 *Massacre in Korea*, the *War* and the *Peace* done in 1952 to decorate a deconsecrated chapel at Vallauris, considered by the artist to be a Temple to Peace, and the 1958 UNESCO mural are his major direct statements on the situation. Such works affirm Picasso's consistency of belief, as stated late in 1937 when he was still involved in the aftermath of Guernica, '. . . I have always believed and still believe, that artists who live and work with spiritual values cannot and should not remain indifferent to a conflict in which the highest values of humanity and civilization are at stake.' The Korean subject is a particularly startling work; in contrast to the dramatic use of light and dark and the expressive emotions found in the great Goya massacre scene, to which it is so often compared, this painting achieves an eerie terror based upon the immobility of the figures who accept their death at the hands of the dehumanized soldiers.

What are the significant facts of Picasso's life in the years since the war? The paramount fact has always been hard work, and this is probably truer than ever. While old friends have been important as a source of pleasure, it seems that they have not been so essential as stimulants as in the past. That he has chosen to live away from Paris since 1945 suggests his need to mitigate the demands from outside so that he can concentrate upon his work.

Picasso's official joining of the Communist party at the end of the war has aroused more interest in the press than any other fact of his post-war life. This was a logical move for the artist given his feelings and attitudes at the time; but the actual decision, as one would expect of such a dedicated person, has had little or no effect upon him or his work. Picasso said at the time: '*My adhesion to the Communist Party is the logical outcome of my whole life. For I am glad to say that I have never considered painting simply as pleasure-giving art, a distraction; I have wanted, by drawing and by colour since those were my weapons, to penetrate always further into the consciousness of the world and of men, so that this understanding may liberate us further each day . . . .*'

Otherwise the principal facts are personal ones, where and with whom Picasso has lived. At the end of the war Picasso established a new relationship with Françoise Gilot; the couple had two children, Claude, born in 1947, and Paloma, born in 1949, and the felicity of the family existence at Vallauris is repeatedly evident in the choice and treatment of subjects in the late forties. The most deeply unhappy period of the artist's life during the last few years was in 1953 when Françoise left him. His distress over this, in addition to his concern about the Korean War, is evident in the painfulness of certain subjects (i.e. no. 254). As had been characteristic of Picasso throughout his life, he has used his art to analyze and cope with conflicting emotions. In this case, the drawings exploring the relationship of the old artist and the young model published by *Verve* apparently helped to create his independence from his distress. Early in 1954 he fell in love with Jacqueline Roque, whom he has since married, and they settled in a new villa, La Californie, at Cannes. They have recently moved to another house near Mougins to achieve greater privacy. The happiness of their relationship has created the background responsible for some of the most contented creations of Picasso's whole career as, at the same time, the pictures become more than ever before a statement of his feelings day by day.

A study of the works of the last fifteen years suggests that Picasso may not be evolving through a succession of styles in order to express his ideas to the same extent that he did earlier in his career. Instead he has explored and synthetized, drawing freely upon his incredible experience with visual images; elements from earlier phases of his career do appear from time to time. Also, as would be expected, the great contrasts of images that can occur within a few days reflecting the dichotomy that is fundamental to Picasso's character continue to be evident. The extent of the extremes found in Picasso's work is seen in no. 267 compared with no. 271 although these two works are months rather than years apart. The 1959 work is the more abstract; Picasso's interest here one feels is in suggesting the essence of femaleness rather than the nature of an individual. The 1960 portrait integrates the side and front views of the head with a new boldness and simplicity that effectively convey the character of the specific woman, even as it reflects Picasso's very personal point of view. The sureness of each picture characterizes the artist's control of his means in recent years.

Whereas earlier in his career the Spaniard shocked for his apparent departure from the object – although in reality he was creating new terms for giving a

more forceful sense of form – in the general adherence to non-representational art today, he might be considered by some almost equally shocking for his tenacity in clinging to the human element. While he is probably not influenced by abstract expressionism as such, he may be said to reflect the attitude of the day which fosters this art form in his more frequent use of much freer brushwork. Such *facture* contributes to the impression of spontaneity evident in great numbers of his recent pictures.

Certain most interesting changes are evident in the choice of subjects and his attitude towards them in the years since the war.

During his youth Picasso studied collections enthusiastically, looking for new ideas and novel approaches to the visual problems facing every artist. African art and the Iberian sculpture were examples of significant influences upon his work. Recently he has again looked to the past, but with a completely different attitude. He has recalled various great works, usually from memory, and has explored their theme or the problems they pose by making restatements which are always related in some way to the original, yet he makes them into highly personal pictures. As the Allies fought on the streets of Paris to free the city, the artist created an appropriately powerful work inspired by a Poussin *Bacchanale*. In 1947 he created ten variations on Cranach's *David and Bathsheba* (no. 245) and subsequently other graphics which reflected Cranach's influence. And in 1950 he created a monumental portrait inspired by El Greco portraits as well as an opulent restatement of Courbet's *Les Demoiselles des bords de la Seine*. Fifteen works, all inspired by Delacroix's great *Femmes d'Alger* in 1955 (no. 263) were followed late in 1957 by forty-four works based upon Velasquez's *Las Meninas* while, most recently, he has made the previously mentioned series inspired by Manet's *Déjeuner* (nos. 272-3). An example of the nature of Picasso's freedom in these restatements is clearly

evident when comparing his series with Delacroix's original which he carefully did not look at as he worked. The positions of the figures are quite different although the same three women and their negro maid are Picasso's point of departure. The Delacroix is essentially a passive conversation piece which nonetheless teems with a subdued opulence and sensuosity, whereas the Picasso is an aggressive voluptuous representation powerfully drawn and vividly coloured with each woman strongly directing her charms at the viewer.

That he should have selected those specific works is in itself also significant. One of the most interesting choices is Velasquez's *Las Meninas,* which was among the earliest great works he would have known, since he must have studied it when he first went to the Prado in 1895. Picasso has always been concerned with the mystery of creation and has frequently dealt with relationships between the artist, the model, the work, and the viewer. Probably no other work of the past is so dominated by these factors as the Velasquez, in which the Princess, posing for the painter, has been interrupted by the arrival of the King and Queen whose images are seen reflected in a mirror. As he painted the different variants, the relationships between the protagonists of Velasquez's work are constantly and dramatically shifting. He pursued the study until the variations on the theme held no more interest; as he has said: '*Pictures* [and, one feels, series] *are never finished in the sense that they suddenly become ready to be signed and framed. They usually come to a halt when the time is ripe, because something happens which breaks the continuity of their development.*'

Two other important series of the past decade are also concerned with the atelier motif, the drawings of 1953 and a series of pictures which show his cluttered studio at La Californie and the view through the window. In a few of the final works in the latter series (no. 264) a woman sits before a canvas on an easel, a canvas which first has an interior painted on it but soon, in the course of reducing the composition to its most fundamental factors, becomes blank. Perhaps related to the various artist-model series, – reasonably so given its 1953 date – is the potentially aggressive work entitled *L'Ombre de l'Artiste* (no. 255) which is a motif repeated at least once again.

The personal felicity of the recent years is repeatedly evident in many works but one particularly interesting area must be referred to although it does not fall into the realm of this exhibition. Landscape has never been a major factor of his work, although from time to time it has been needed as a release from current problems, whether visual or otherwise. Since the war his landscapes have been more important in his work than ever before. There are wonderful landscapes of Vallauris and, even more lyrical are the 1957 views from his window with doves resting on the sill which clearly served as a respite from the intensity of the Velasquez variants.

A period of notable diversity stylistically took place in the late 1940's particularly 1948 and 1949, when in a brief time he explored a variety of expressions, often ones reverting to past phases. Also interesting is the sudden intensity with which he explored other media. He settled at Vallauris because of the pottery done in this village; he quickly learned the art and realized remarkable works that clearly delighted him, given their frequent humour, even as he solved the problems of integrating his designs to the forms he had created. These were also years of exploration in the lithographic medium, which, when he began in November 1945, he had not touched since 1930. In the following nine years he created 262 prints, many of which went through several quite different states. Also, about 1950-1951 was a remarkable period for the sculptures that he created (nos. 249, 250), some of the most important ones of his whole career since they

are major monumental conceptions rather than, as many, *jeux d'esprit*.

Picasso is now over eighty years of age. His work is dominated by a youthfulness based upon an intense joy of living and a constant curiosity. One wonders, however, whether a certain nostalgia for the memories of his own youth does not enter often into his thinking, whether the nationalistic element in his make-up is not stronger. That he should choose to live in the south of France and, perhaps more interesting, that he should have purchased the Château Vauvenargues in a part of France that has certain analogies with the landscape of the Spain that he has most loved, may reflect such feelings. He has always had a passionate enthusiasm for the bullfight, but never has it emerged as such an important subject in his thinking as in the recent paintings and even more in the brilliant drawings and in the linocuts of 1959 and 1960. This cannot be chance. In the last few years, as he has achieved a brilliant pictorial synthesis in which form and expression are powerfully merged to create a succession of strong pictures, he has also created a basic statement in which the frankness and the mystery, the moodiness and the splendours characteristic of Spanish art for centuries are epitomized.

There can be little doubt that Picasso is the most powerful personality of our century in the visual arts. His work is in the very greatest humanist tradition, even as it is thoroughly contemporary in its exploration of man in terms of the conflicts and the adjustments required of him in this century. Picasso has been fortunate in being among those few artists to have experienced long life as well as the freedom necessary to achieve the consummation that his rare abilities deserve.

1 BY LAMP LIGHT/
HOMME A LA LAMPE

Barcelona 1898 / Z I: 6

oil on canvas, 39-1/2 x 24-1/2 in.,
100.2 x 62.2 cm.

signed 'P Ruiz Picasso' lower right

Provenance: Llobet collection,
Barcelona; unknown private
collection; acquired by present
owners November 1961

Picasso Exhibitions: New York 1962,
Tribute, Knoedler no. 2

lent by Mr. and Mrs. Monroe Geller

To Picasso at seventeen man could be,
as he is here, a body seen in space. But
that space, with its light from the lamp
on the writing table, is suggestive of
loneliness and melancholy.

The man who sat for this work was
Josef Cardona Iturro, a sculptor who
was a little older than Picasso and is
said (Vallentin p. 28) to have introduced
the younger man to the German
equivalent of Pre-Raphaelite art, the
work of the Nazarenes. When Picasso
returned to Barcelona in 1898, after
several months' convalescence in Horta
de San Juan from the scarlet fever to
which he had succumbed in Madrid in
the spring, he used a small room in the
Cardona apartment (no. 1 calle de
Escudillero Blanco) as a studio. It was
probably in that year that he painted
this work.

2 PORTRAIT OF JOSEF CARDONA

Barcelona 1898 / not in Z

conte crayon, 15 x 12 in., 38 x 30.4 cm.

signed 'Al volgut amich Cardona–P. Ruiz Picasso –'

Related Works: no. 1; Z VI: 264

Picasso Exhibitions: Los Angeles 1961, UCLA no. 48

lent by Miss Margaret Mallory

This drawing of Cardona is a portrait, his individuality suggested by contrasting his casual, battered working-man's clothes with his sharply defined, elongated Spanish face. Although his brows are decisive and quizzical, Cardona's eyes are surprisingly vague. And there is a certain weariness in the way he holds his head and shoulders.

Young Picasso's drawing style was harsh, angular and accented. There was also a sense of rhythm in the lines, for example in the relation of the eyebrows to Cardona's moustache.

3 PORTRAIT OF E. TORENT

Barcelona 1899 / not in Z

charcoal, 19-1/4 x 12-3/4 in.,
48.8 x 32.3 cm.

signed 'A mi amigo/E. Torent/P. Ruiz
Picasso' lower left

Provenance: acquired by the museum
1938

lent by The Detroit Institute of Arts

Nothing has been discovered about
E. Torent – but his portrait is typical
of many Picasso made during these
Barcelona years. Picasso had an
uncanny gift for picking out the
characteristic features of a human
face, for noticing personal idiosyn-
crasies of toilet like the shape of
Torent's hair or the particular upward
turn of his moustaches. He also noticed
how his sitter held his body (the way
Torent, for example, put his right hand
in his pocket) and exactly how he wore
his clothes. From such observations
and the sensitive if brusque movements
of his piece of charcoal, Picasso created
a sequence of highly individual portrait
drawings which can rival those the
Frenchman Ingres had made in Rome
and Florence considerably earlier in
the century.

For other formal portrait drawings of
this same time see: Z I: 13, 18, 29;
Z VI: 99, 196, 247, 248, 249, 252, 254,
263, 264, 265, 266, 267, 268, 272, 286,
287, 297, 298, 300, 303, 304, 321, 370,
372, 399, 1454 and others not in Zervos.

4 PORTRAIT OF MATEO FERNANDEZ
   DE SOTO

Barcelona 1899 / Z VI: 269

charcoal, 19-3/4 x 13-1/4 in.,
50 x 33.5 cm.

signed 'P. Ruiz Picasso' upper left

Related Works: Z VI: 120, 165;
Z I 86, 94

Provenance: Paul Chadourne, Paris

lent by Mrs. Raymond Goodrich

Mateo Ferandez de Soto, who was a
sculptor and one of two brothers who
were among Picasso's closest Barcelona
friends, was also to go to Paris for a
few years where Picasso's mistress,
Fernande, (Olivier p. 210) met him and
wrote about him, 'Je crois que Picasso
l'aimait plus que d'autres, peut-être à
cause de sa faiblesse physique; il était
petit, étriqué, pâle, minable.'

   In costume and mood this drawing
seems related to a drawing Picasso
made of another friend, Jamie Sabartés,
in 1899. The poet Sabartés is dressed in
a cloak and wears a crown of laurel,
his pale profile and dark body
silhouetted against the gravestones of
a cemetery. In these two portraits the
mysterious cloaks, luminous old faces
and frail bodies seem intended to
exploit – if not to caricature – the two
young men as disciples of a typical
fin de siècle decadence. Picasso even
inscribed the drawing of Sabartés
'Poeta Decadente.'

5 THE BULLFIGHT/
   LA COURSE DE TAUREAUX

   Barcelona 1900/not in Z

   pastel and gouache, 18 x 27 in.,
   45.6 x 68.5 cm.
   signed 'P. Ruiz Picasso' lower left

Provenance: acquired by present
owners March 1959

Picasso Exhibitions: New York 1962,
Tribute, Knoedler no. 6

lent by Mr. and Mrs. Henry John
Heinz II

Picasso, who had been introduced to
the bullfight by his father as a child,
told his biographer Roland Penrose
(Penrose p. 58), 'People think that I
painted pictures of bullfights in those
days after they were over. Not at all, I
painted them the day before and sold
them to anyone so as to have enough
money to buy a ticket.' This pastel
seems the product of such anticipation,
the faceless figures not very clear but
with a luster, everything assembled
around the sand and toward the
opening through which the bull, who
will bring both violence and a meaning
to life, is expected to appear.

6 STREET SCENE / SCENE DANS LA RUE

Paris 1900 / Z VI: 302

oil on canvas, 18-1/2 x 25-1/2 in.,
47 x 64.7 cm.

signed 'P. R. Picasso' lower left

Provenance: Harriet Lane Levy, San
Francisco; acquired by the museum
1950

Picasso Exhibitions: New York 1939,
MMA no. 7

lent by The San Francisco Museum
of Art

A sense of loneliness and melancholy, which can be detected in Picasso's earlier work, is very apparent here. The heavy, listless bodies and the shapeless garments of the man on the sidewalk and the mother and child on the road, suggest human beings without vitality and without any real identities (we cannot even see their faces). The Montmartre streets around them, painted by Picasso in shapes as limp as theirs, only enhance the sense of the vagueness (if not quite the futility) of human life.

The *Street Scene* shows the influence of two artists on Picasso at this time, the Swiss socialist illustrator, Théophile Steinlen (1859-1923), whose works we are told Picasso already knew in Barcelona, and the Spaniard, Isidro Nonell (1873-1911), whose apartment on the rue Gabrielle in Montmartre Picasso inherited on this visit to Paris.

7 WOMAN SEATED/FEMME ASSISE
Paris 1900 or Madrid 1901/Z VI: 335

conte crayon and pastel, 16 x 20-1/2 in.
40.6 x 52 cm.

signed 'Picasso' lower left

Provenance: Robert Lebel, Paris;
acquired by present owner
January 1957

lent by Mrs. John A. MacAulay

This pastel of a woman has the
repressed energy of many of the
illustrations (Z VI: 371, 373, 393, 394)
Picasso published in *Arte Joven* in
Madrid in 1901, but which he had
anticipated already in the sketches he
had made on letters to friends from
Paris in 1900 (Z VI: 289, 290, 293, 294).
Even though the pastel is reminiscent
of the work of Toulouse-Lautrec which
Picasso very much admired and was
able to study in Paris, and particularly
of that profile figure of a woman seated
at a café which is called *Gueule de bois*
(Fogg Art Museum), and which used
to be in the Van Horne collection in
Montreal, Picasso's effect here is not
one of slovenly apathy like Toulouse's
but rather of a nervous tension and
anxiety which has not quite succumbed
to despair.

8 NUDE WOMAN WITH CATS/
NU ET CHATS

Paris 1901 / Z I: 93

oil on cardboard, 17-1/2 x 16 in.,
44.4 x 40.6 cm.

signed 'Picasso' lower right

Provenance: Paul Guillaume, Paris
(Zervos); Reinhardt Galleries,
New York; acquired by the museum
1942

lent by The Art Institute of Chicago
the Amy McCormick Memorial
Collection

Nothing could be further removed from classical ideals of female beauty than this miserable, crouching figure who, from embarrassment or from cold, tries to conceal her nudity, and looks unhappily beyond the playing kittens. She seems an Eve without the memory of an Eden.

When one speaks of Picasso's conventional academic art schooling it was not one, apparently, which included the female nude. There are early studies of the male nude, from life and from works of sculpture, but none of women. His experience in art schools probably merely represented a continuation of the traditional Spanish prudery about nude women. And Picasso, affected in one way or another by this prudery, painted his first female nudes in Paris either according to motives established by Degas (Z I: 102, 103; Z VI: 377, 397), in positions of mundane realism (Z I: 106) or as devastatingly ugly women of the streets (Z I: 48, 104).

WOMAN WITH PLUMED HAT/
TETE DE FEMME

WOMAN WITH JEWELLED COLLAR/
FEMME AU COLLIER DE GEMMES

COURTESAN WITH JEWELLED COLLAR/
L'HETAIRE

9 WOMAN WITH PLUMED HAT/
TETE DE FEMME

Madrid 1901/Z I: 39

oil on canvas, 18-3/8 x 15-1/8 in.,
46.6 x 38.3 cm.

signed 'P. R. Picasso/Madrid'
lower right

Provenance: Reinhardt Galleries, New
York; Dalzell Hatfield, Los Angeles

Picasso Exhibitions: San Antonio 1954,
no. 3; New York 1962, Tribute,
Knoedler no. 4

lent by The Marion Koogler McNay
Art Institute

9

In spite of the strokes of paint and an
aura of plumes, artificial flowers,
jewels, powder and rouge, it is
apparent that Picasso did not have
much more respect for the successful
courtesan dressed than he did for her
humbler sister nude.

   This work has usually been dated
1900, ignoring the inscription 'Madrid'
in the lower right corner which is
cropped in most photographs but not
in Zervos (I: 39).

10

Remembering the head of the courtesan
he had painted in Madrid, Picasso in
Paris did another head of another
courtesan with the same jewelled collar
but with a simpler hat surmounted now
by a great bird of prey. Everything has
become bolder, coarser and stronger –
the features of the face, the continuous
rhythmic movements through her hair
and her hat, the shapes and the colour,
and finally the insensitive, predatory
expression of her face.

The largest and most urbane of the
three heads of courtesans exhibited
here was shown at Berthe Weill's in
Paris in 1902 and called 'L'Hétaïre.'
She is close to the woman in the Zacks
picture; and both seem intimately
related in features and handling to
Picasso's terrifying bestial nude of the
period, *La Gommeuse* (Z I: 104), and
to the sullen female companion of the
harlequin in Leningrad's *Les Deux
Saltimbanques* (Z I: 92). The bird on
this courtesan's hat is bolder than it is
in the other work and even more
predatory; it anticipates the horror of
Picasso's macabre little sketchbook
drawing (Z I: 149) of a raven sucking
blood from the forehead of a still, bald
and bearded man from 1902.

10 WOMAN WITH JEWELLED COLLAR/
FEMME AU COLLIER DE GEMMES
Paris 1901 / Z VI: 385

oil on cardboard, 17-1/4 x 14-1/4 in.,
43.7 x 36.1 cm.

signed 'Picasso' upper left

Provenance: Mr. and Mrs. Q. A. Shaw
McKean, Boston; Carstairs Gallery,
New York

Picasso Exhibitions: Hartford 1934,
no. 3 (mistakenly as Z I: 42); New
York 1936, Seligmann No. 1

lent from the Collection of Ayala and
Sam Zacks

11 COURTESAN WITH JEWELLED
COLLAR/ L'HETAIRE
Paris 1901 / Z I: 42

oil on canvas, 25-3/4 x 21-1/2 in.,
65.3 x 54.5 cm.

signed 'Picasso' upper left

Provenance: Ricardo Viñés, Paris; Mr.
and Mrs. George Gard de Sylva, Los

Angeles; given to the museum 1946

Picasso Exhibitions: Paris 1902; New
York 1947, Knoedler no. 8; San
Antonio 1954, no. 5; Los Angeles
1961, UCLA no. 1

lent by The Los Angeles County
Museum of Art
the Mr. and Mrs. George Gard de
Sylva Collection

12 CHILD HOLDING A DOVE/
    L'ENFANT AU PIGEON

Paris 1901 / Z I: 83

oil on canvas, 28-3/4 x 21-1/4 in.,
73 x 54 cm.

signed 'Picasso' centre left

Provenance: Paul Rosenberg, Paris;
Alex Reid, Glasgow; Mrs. R. A.
Workman, London; Reid & Lefèvre,
London; Samuel Courtauld, London
1928; acquired by present owner 1947

Picasso Exhibitions: London 1960, Arts
Council no.14

lent by Christabel, Lady Aberconway

CHILD HOLDING A DOVE/
L'ENFANT AU PIGEON

Holding a Dove and its curvalinear forms mark a step in Picasso's movement into the Blue Period although this palette is not as cold nor the mood as somber as a genuinely Blue period work.

13 CROUCHING WOMAN/
LA MISEREUSE ACCROUPIE

Barcelona 1902/Z I: 121

oil on canvas, 39-7/8 x 26 in.,
101.2 x 66 cm.

signed 'Picasso' upper left

Provenance: Justin K. Thannhauser, Münich; Professor and Mrs. Bruno Mendel; anonymous gift to the museum 1963

The Art Gallery of Toronto

This pretty and much loved picture represents a tender, helpless innocence as extreme in its way as the evil of the prostitutes is in another. It brings together a child, and Picasso all his life was to feel great affection for children, and a dove which has always been an important symbol for him. As a member of a Catholic society Picasso could not have been unconscious of its Christian meaning. It also had a more personal meaning for him, however, because his father had rarely painted anything but dovecotes of pigeons and is said to have given up painting completely in 1894, when he realized his thirteen-year-old son could paint these birds more convincingly than he. In recent years Picasso's doves have become political symbols – but appropriately of peace. In addition, Picasso has also remained fascinated by the relationship between a child and an animal, although the child has seldom been as gently protective toward his pet as here.

In its very sweetness this painting suggests that Picasso was influenced by one of the French followers of Gauguin who formed the group known as the Nabis; this was Maurice Denis (1870-1943). It also suggests the same painters in its flatness and the heavy, continuous languid contours; it could illustrate Denis' advice as early as 1890, 'Remember that a picture . . . is essentially a plane surface covered with colours assembled in a certain order.'

The gentle pathos of the *Child*

CROUCHING WOMAN/
LA MISEREUSE ACCROUPIE

With Picasso's return to Barcelona in January 1902 he produced works of an extraordinary melancholy and compassion – using those blues which gave the name to the period, of which his friend the poet Apollinaire said 'For a year [actually it was longer] Picasso lived this type of painting, blue as the humid depth of an abyss, and full of pity.' Many Spanish influences can be found in these paintings – El Greco in the modelling of the draperies, the Barcelona painter, Isidro Nonell (1873-1911) in the concept of the figures, wooden Gothic sculpture in the severe, withdrawn faces. That in the twentieth century a mendicant like this should have been given a spiritual rather than a social significance seems Spanish.

14 LA SOUPE

Paris 1902-1903 / Z I: 131

oil on canvas, 14-5/8 x 17-3/4 in.,
37 x 45 cm.

not signed or dated

Related Works: Z VI: 409, 418, 420,
474; Z I: 192, 163; Z VI: 435, 436

Provenance: Klaus Sternheim, Paris;
von Ripper; Knoedler, New York

Picasso Exhibitions: New York 1947,
Knoedler no. 13

lent by Mrs. Harold Crang

This small painting shows Picasso giving
the daily life of the poor a ritualistic
character reminiscent of religious art.
It is related to a painting in Leningrad
(Z I: 163) of two women meeting which
Picasso called *Les Deux Soeurs* (Z VI:
436) but which suggests a *Visitation*.
Although the preparatory drawings
for this, one of which (Z VI: 409) is
inscribed 'December 1902,' have a
sturdy realism, there is a certain
mannerism in the painting, particularly
in the bent figure of the draped woman.

15 SEATED WOMAN / FEMME ASSISE

Paris or Barcelona 1903 / not in Z

oil on canvas, 32 x 21-1/4 in.,
81.2 x 54 cm.

not signed or dated

Related Works: Z I: 133

Provenance: Ambroise Vollard, Paris;
acquired by present owner 1950

lent by Mr. G. Hamilton Southam

The people in Picasso's Blue Period
works are frequently withdrawn into
an almost catatonic state. The soft,
boneless bodies of the women are
arched into positions which seem to
demand a child at their breasts or at
least in their arms; the lack of a child
in this work and in no. 13 adds to
the sense of their loneliness. Their
bodies are passive, dejected, incapable
of movement, their attention is withdrawn from any outer communication.
Compassionate and tender as Picasso
is in his painting of them, they seem
the symbols of despair.

   This work has a greater delicacy in
contour and tonality than no. 13
which suggests the transition into the
following Rose Period.

MASK OF A MAN WITH A BROKEN
NOSE/UN MASQUE D'HOMME AU
NEZ CASSE

ANGEL FERNANDEZ DE SOTO/
THE ABSINTHE DRINKER

18 MEDITATION/CONTEMPLATION

Rodin's famous *Man with the Broken Nose* of 1864, which Picasso could have seen in the Louvre, must have suggested this work. In modelling Picasso was as vigorous as Rodin, but as he pressed his thumb down to suggest the forehead's frown or the crease in the cheek, he could work more freely and abstractly in producing the dramatic planes of the ravaged face. He exaggerated the size of the eyes and gave the mouth that mobile and enigmatic form one finds in some of Picasso's Blue Period works.

The dating of this mask is a problem. Since the cast was inscribed 04:1905, it has been assumed that Picasso modelled it in 1904 and Vollard cast it in 1905. Zervos dates a watercolour for it (Z VI: 597) Barcelona 1903, and there is some reason to assume, from the boldness of the mask's modelling and its tragic mood, that it comes from that year. Fernande (Olivier p. 59) calls it 'un masque de toréador espagnol au nez cassé qui est d'une force, d'une vie très intense,' thus apparently identifying it with Spain.

Angel Fernandez de Soto was the second of the two brothers who frequented the café Els Quatre Gats in Barcelona. Mr. Richardson (New York 1962, Tribute) quotes Picasso saying of this sitter, 'Angel de Soto was my best friend in Barcelona. His one desire in life was to please me. You can't imagine how loyal and good-hearted he was . . . but he had a horror of work and never did anything except maybe hire a tail-coat and go on as an extra in a musical comedy.' In this portrait of 1903 Picasso used the asymmetry and mobility of the head to paint a powerful portrait of both the wastrel and the friend.

This portrait of Angel de Soto is one of a series Picasso did of close friends at café tables. The best known is the 1901 painting of the poet, Jaime Sabartés, which is often called the *Glass of Beer* (Z I: 97, The Hermitage Museum, Leningrad). He had also painted two other poet friends in cafés, in 1899 Rafael Nogeruas Oller with an unknown woman at Els Quatre Gats (Z I: 21) and in 1902 the elfin-faced Cornutti with a sullen woman of the streets (Z I: 182). In 1903 he caricatured himself and two of his closest artist friends, Sebastian Juñer and de Soto, at a café table (Z VI: 147) and then apparently decided to paint each of them with an equivocal companion. Juñer's portrait (Z I: 174, David E. Bright collection, Los Angeles) was finished with a woman rather like the woman in the print of the next year,

The Frugal Repast (no. 19), beside him. In 1904 Picasso painted himself (Z I: 275, Mr. and Mrs. Charles S. Payson collection, New York) as a debonnaire, disillusioned harlequin with a woman he told Mr. Richardson (New York 1962, Tribute, Knoedler no. 16) was the one for whom a friend of his had committed suicide. A quick sketch of Angel de Soto with a frivolous female companion (Galerie Rosengart, Lucerne, illustrated Millier) suggests that Picasso had considered the same form of double portrait for the third of the trio in the caricature but had apparently decided to eliminate the woman, who in all these portraits seems alien to the sitter and to society, and to concentrate upon his friend in the neutral, and to Picasso, melancholy environment of the café.

Paris 1904/Z I: 235

watercolour, 13-3/4 x 10-1/8 in., 34.8 x 25.6 cm.

signed 'Picasso' lower right

Provenance: Raoul Pellequer, Paris; Jules Furthman

Picasso Exhibitions: New York 1936, Seligmann no. 18; New York 1957, MMA p. 23; Philadelphia 1958, no. 16; New York 1962, Tribute, Knoedler no. 20

lent by Mrs. Bertram Smith

16　MASK OF A MAN WITH A BROKEN
NOSE / UN MASQUE D'HOMME AU
NEZ CASSE

1903 / not in Z

bronze, 7-3/4 in. high, 19.6 cm.

cast by Vollard 1905
inscribed on cast: 04: 1905

lent from the Collection of
Joseph H. Hirshhorn

17　ANGEL FERNANDEZ DE SOTO /
THE ABSINTHE DRINKER

Barcelona 1903 / Z I: 201

oil on canvas, 27-1/2 x 21-3/4 in.,
69.7 x 55.2 cm.

signed 'Picasso/1903' upper right

Related Works: Z VI: 147, 278, 557;
Z I: 174; drawing in Rosengart
Collection, Lucerne; caricature
inscribed 'Patas' illustrated in
Merli p. 16

Provenance: Paul von Mendelssohn,
Germany; Justin K. Thannhauser,
Lucerne; William H. Taylor, West

Lucerne; William H. Taylor, West
Chester, Pennsylvania; acquired by
present owners 1946

Picasso Exhibitions: New York 1947,
Knoedler no. 15; New York 1962,
Tribute, Knoedler no. 18

The *Frugal Repast* can be used to study the transformations of the character and meaning of certain figures and situations in Picasso's work. Not much more can be said about the woman than that she belongs to a disturbingly androgynous type who appears in Picasso's paintings in 1904, after he had made studies leading in her direction in Barcelona in 1903; her most famous sisters are probably the *Ironer* belonging to the Thannhauser Foundation, the *Woman with a Crow* in Toledo and the watercolour of *Two Nude Women* (Z VI: 652) in a private collection in Paris. Her blind companion has, however, a more complicated history.

The compassion Picasso felt for mankind during the Blue Period was inevitably directed toward the man who had lost – what to Picasso was the most important of the senses – sight. In Barcelona in 1903 he had painted and drawn many blind men, seeing them as bearded and clean shaven, alone at a meal, bothered by children as they ate, as forlorn beggars with a young boy as a companion or, in the famous work in The Art Institute of Chicago (Z I: 202) as a musician. Although he sometimes painted his blind man frontally, he gradually developed an image of him in a profile position with a slightly opened mouth. When Picasso moved to Paris in April 1904 this image persisted and exists, of course, in *The Frugal Repast*. It is also found in a simple drawing (Z VI: 630) dated May 6, 1904 of a seated, bearded blind man who is emaciated but not undignified, and in another drawing (Z VI: 631) in which the same man seems to be walking slowly, about to touch the head of a young girl who stands before him with a simplicity and stillness of a young Tahitian by Gauguin. Finally, perhaps in 1905, he is given a crown, a pink jester's suit

and a music box, and a little boy in a harlequin's suit sits beside him as a companion; this is the gouache, *Acrobat Sitting with a Child*, in the Kunsthaus, Zürich (Z VI: 798).

As the blind man gains in dignity and bearing, as he can be mocked a little as he is by the bowler hat in *The Frugal Repast*, as he responds to the world beyond himself through his hands as he does in the drawing with the little girl or with the woman in the etching, as he is finally transformed by the costume which makes him something of a jester and more of a king, he reveals Picasso breaking through the trance-like pity of his pure Blue Period works.

This etching is one of many works Picasso made (see no. 17) of couples in cafés, probably originally inspired by the type established by Degas in his 1876 *l'Absinthe* in the Louvre and carried on by Toulouse-Lautrec in his 1891 *A la Mie* in the Museum of Fine Arts, Boston. If it is compared with any of Picasso's earlier treatments of this theme it reveals how much crisper and more angular his work had become, how much more sharply he distinguished one space from another. The bodies are also highly articulated and so boney and elongated that various authors including Barr (p. 29) and Blunt and Pool (nos. 123-132) have used Gothic sculpture, Mannerist art, El Greco and Dürer to explain them. And there is not the terrible apathy of the Blue Period works. Strange though the man and woman of *The Frugal Repast* may be, they respond with something besides boredom and malevolence to the world around them – and frail as their bodies are, they are sufficiently articulated so that the blind man and his companion could contemplate moving from that environment.

19 THE FRUGAL REPAST /
LE REPAS FRUGAL

Paris 1904 / G 2

etching on zinc, 18-1/4 x 14-7/8 in.,
47 x 37.7 cm.

lent by Mr. M. F. Feheley

20 MOTHER AND CHILD/
MÈRE ET ENFANT

Paris 1904 / Z I: 220

black crayon, 13-1/2 x 10-1/2 in.,
34.2 x 26.6 cm.

signed 'Picasso/1904' lower right
verso with drawing of nude man

Related Works: Z I: 299

Provenance: Vignier; acquired by
Paul J. Sachs 1929

Picasso Exhibitions: Hartford 1934,
no. 82; New York 1939, MMA no. 23;
San Antonio 1954, no. 6; Houston
1955, no. 3

lent by The Fogg Art Museum,
Harvard University
Meta and Paul J. Sachs Collection

Picasso's 1904 works, like this sensitive drawing of a *Mother and Child*, hint at pleasanter possibilities for mankind. His style is more delicate and more refined, as if beauty itself could be admitted as a possibility now; the line is even like a caress. The attenuated bodies he drew and painted may not have borne much flesh or muscle, but their skeletons are apparent through the skin as if to suggest these figures would not be the victims of the complete inertia of those in the Blue Period paintings. And the compassion of the earlier works has been changed to a tenderness which does not weigh as heavily upon man.

21 PROFILE OF A WOMAN/
TÊTE DE FEMME DE PROFIL

Paris 1905 / G 7

dry point on copper, 11-1/2 x 9-7/8 in.,
29.2 x 25 cm.

lent by Mr. M. F. Feheley

THE BATH / LE BAIN

MOTHER COMBING HER HAIR /
LA TOILETTE DE LA MERE

SALOME

22 THE BATH / LE BAIN
1905 / G 14, Z VI: 694
drypoint, 13-9/16 x 11-7/16 in.,
34.4 x 28.9 cm.
signed 'Picasso/1905' upper right
Related Works: Z VI: 696
lent by Mr. Vincent Tovell

Works like these carry us into the Rose
Period in which Picasso often painted,
etched and drew itinerant circus
families with great delicacy and
tenderness. The sense of a family's
relationship, particularly of the mother
to the child she is bathing, seems
happier than it had ever been in
Picasso's work. Gertrude Stein with her
usual wisdom said of this period (Stein
p. 21), 'When I say that the rose period
is light and happy everything is relative,
the subjects which were happy ones
were a little sad, the families of the
harlequins were wretched families but
from Picasso's point of view it was a
light happy joyous period and a period
when he contented himself with seeing
things as anybody did.'

23
Picasso's friend, the poet Apollinaire,
was to write later about this print and
the related gouache (*The Cubist
Painters,* tr. by Lionel Abel, New York:
Wittenborn, 1944), 'In the square
room, paternity transfigures the
harlequin, whose wife bathes with cold
water and admires her figure, as frail
and slim as her husband, the puppet.'
He also wrote, 'Some harlequins match
the splendor of the women, whom they
resemble, being neither male nor
female . . . the sexes are indistinct . . .
taciturn harlequins have their cheeks
and foreheads paled by morbid
sensuality.'

25
Picasso exploited imperfections in the
copper plate to suggest the vanished
veils of Salomé and he used, as his
model for Herod, the fat figure of a
clown who appears in his *Family of
Saltimbanques* of the same year
(National Gallery of Washington, Z I:
285). In spite of the understated
implications of the subject Picasso
encourages us to take pleasure in the
exquisite line and the compact diagonal
band of the composition.

24 LES SALTIMBANQUES
1905 / G 9, Z VI: 701
drypoint, 11-3/8 x 12-7/8 in.,
28.8 x 32.6 cm.
signed 'Picasso/1905' lower right
lent by Mr. Vincent Tovell

23 MOTHER COMBING HER HAIR/
LA TOILETTE DE LA MERE

1905 / G 15

etching on zinc, 9-1/4 x 6-15/16 in.,
23.5 x 17.6 cm.

Related Works: Z I: 298

lent by Mr. M. F. Feheley

25 SALOME

1905 / G 17

drypoint, 15-3/4 x 13-3/4 in.,
40 x 34.8 cm.

signed 'Picasso/1905' upper right

lent by Mr. M. F. Feheley

26 HEAD OF A JESTER / TETE DE FOU

1905 / Z I: 322

bronze, 16-1/4 in. high, 41.2 cm.

cast by Vollard 1905, signed 'Picasso'

Related Works: Z I: 243, 293

lent from the Collection of
Joseph H. Hirshhorn

This piece of sculpture, which was cast
by Vollard in 1905, was probably
modelled by Picasso early in that year.
Its surfaces are rough and its contours
indefinite so that in catching the
nuances of changing light it gives an
impression of the mercurial nature of
this jester with the ageless face.

27 BOY WITH A BOUQUET/
    JEUNE HOMME AU BOUQUET

1905 / Z I: 262

gouache, 25-1/2 x 21-3/8 in.,
64.7 x 54.2 cm.

signed 'Picasso' lower right

Provenance: Mrs. John D. McIlhenny,
Philadelphia

Picasso Exhibitions: New York 1947,
Knoedler no. 20; Philadelphia 1958,
no. 20

lent by Mrs. John Wintersteen

This boy, whose features are close to
those of many youths Picasso drew
and painted in 1905, particularly
in preparation for the unrealized
Watering Place, has an expression
which is enigmatic, equivocal, even
teasing, and a beauty as ephemeral as
the flowers he holds in his hand. It is
possible that Picasso may have painted
him as a parallel to the sturdier, full-
length *Girl with a Basket of Flowers*
(Z I: 256) of the same year, which was
the first work the Steins were to buy
from Picasso.

28 FAMILY WITH A CROW/
FAMILLE A LA CORNEILLE
1905 / Z VI: 703

pen and ink and crayon,
12-7/8 x 9-1/2 in., 32.6 x 24 cm.

signed 'Picasso' lower right

Related Works: Z I: 279

Provenance: acquired by the museum
1960

Picasso Exhibitions: New York 1962,
MMA

lent by The Museum of Modern Art,
New York
the John S. Newberry Collection

The casualness with which the figures
in this drawing focus upon the pet crow
represents a change in Picasso's work
which must have taken place in 1905
itself. The crow, which was probably
modelled on the pet one at Le Lapin
Agile, seems a perfectly natural,
sceptical bird and not, like the one in
Picasso's famous 1904 gouache in
Toledo (Z I: 240), fraught with all kinds
of disturbing psychological meaning.
Similarly the figures themselves are
sturdier and less self-conscious than the
members of the Saltimbanque families
in the etchings Picasso had dated 1905.

This is related to another drawing
(Z I: 279) with certain links with
Picasso's most ambitious work of 1905,
the *Family of Saltimbanques* (Z I: 285)
in the National Gallery of Washington
(Chester Dale Collection). Both seem
stylistically related to another group
of drawings, all about 40 x 30 cm. (Z VI:
460, 700, 739, 740, 809, 810, 845, 846,
878, 879, 880, 881, 882) which are
scratchily drawn with the pen and in
which the figures seem to show great
pleasure in the movement of their
sturdy bodies.

29 NUDE YOUNG MAN ON HORSE-
BACK / JEUNE HOMME ET CHEVAL

Paris, 1905 / Z VI: 682

charcoal, 18-3/8 x 12 in., 46.6 x 30.4 cm.

signed 'Picasso' lower left in 1937

Related Works: Z I: 265

Provenance: Pierre Matisse, Paris;
acquired by present owners 1937

Picasso Exhibitions: New York 1939,
MMA no. 53; New York 1957, MMA
p. 27; Philadelphia 1958, no. 19

lent by Mr. and Mrs. John W.
Warrington

In 1905 Picasso worked toward a
painting called *The Watering Place*
which was never realized beyond a
gouache composition (Z I: 265). The
studies for it, however, including the
Boy Leading a Horse (Z I: 264) in the
collection of Mr. and Mrs. William S.
Paley, New York and the *Youth in Blue*
(Z I: 271) in the Warburg Collection,
are among the most beautiful of his
Rose Period works. One of these is
this drawing which reveals Picasso's
new pleasure in the beauty of the
human body, in the rhythmic way it
could move and in the way he himself
could draw. In the realism and discipline of that pleasure it recalls in spirit
parts of the Parthenon frieze which
Picasso as a student had studied from
plaster casts.

SEATED NUDE ARRANGING HAIR /
FEMME AU PEIGNE

30 SEATED NUDE ARRANGING HAIR /
FEMME AU PEIGNE

1905 / not in Z

brush and rose-red watercolour,
15-5/8 x 10-3/4 in., 39.6 x 27.2 cm.

not signed or dated

Provenance: Miss Etta and Dr. Claribel
Cone, Baltimore; acquired by the
museum 1950

lent by The Baltimore Museum of Art
Cone Collection

During the summer of 1905, Picasso
visited a Dutch friend at Schooredam
in Holland. According to Penrose (p.
113), 'For one month Picasso gazed
in amazement at the flatness of the
landscape and the opulent forms of the
Dutch girls, head and shoulders taller
than himself.' What Penrose calls the
'opulence' of the Dutch women can
be seen in this drawing in which
Picasso made the contours of the fleshy
body so energetic, the sanguine of the
ink so warm, the expression of her face
so gentle and her gesture so natural
that the drawing has a human and
visual richness to which the adjective
'opulent' might legitimately apply. It
contrasts dramatically with Chicago's
Nude Woman with Cats of 1909 (no. 8).

31 NUDE WITH HANDS CROSSED/
NU AUX MAINS SERREES

1905/Z I: 310

gouache on canvas, 37-3/4 x 29-3/4 in.,
95.8 x 75.5 cm.

signed 'à mon vrai ami Picasso,
1er janvier 1907'on the back

Studies: Z VI. 900

Related Works: Z I: 326, 327;
Z VI: 517, 779, 882, 1464

Provenance: Galerie Rosengart,
Lucerne; acquired by present owners
August 14, 1956

lent from the Collection of
Ayala and Sam Zacks

Although Picasso was already showing
an awareness of the possible beauty of
the female nude in some of his works
like the etching of the Harlequin family
of 1905 (no. 23), it may have been his
trip to the Netherlands that summer
which persuaded him to concentrate
upon the solidity and the sensuality of
the female body. This nude, which
would have been painted later in 1905,
has some of the solidity and all of the
modesty and gentleness of Picasso's
Dutch paintings. At the same time in
the frontality and dignity there are
suggestions of classical art which its
pale terracotta colour deliberately
emphasizes, as if in its very paleness it
were an evocation of the ideal past.

   The drawing, which could be a study
for this (Z VI: 882), is related
stylistically to a drawing connected
with the *Family With a Crow* (no. 28).

32 YOUNG WOMAN STANDING IN
PROFILE TO THE LEFT / JEUNE FEMME
DEBOUT DE PROFIL

Gosol 1906 / not in Z

black chalk, 23-1/2 x 17-3/4 in.,
59.6 x 45 cm.

signed 'Picasso' twice on the back,
upper and lower left

Related Works: two drawings, Cone
Collection, The Baltimore Museum of
Art; Z VI: 633, 882

Provenance: Huldschinsky, Berlin;
Mrs. A. Furstenberg, Amsterdam;
acquired by the museum from
Wildenstein, London, 1953

lent by The National Gallery of
Canada, Ottawa

During the summer of 1906 at Gosol,
which Fernande has described as such
a happy one for Picasso, he made
several drawings of a dignified and
graceful peasant woman. The largest
and perhaps the most beautiful of
these is this sensitive, understated chalk
drawing in The National Gallery of
Canada. The contours of her body swell
with the beauty and discipline of an
early Greek *Kouros* and she walks with
such an innate dignity and measured
tread that she could be bearing a gift
to Athena on the Panathenaic frieze
of the Parthenon.

One drawing illustrated in Zervos
(Z VI: 882) has in the centre a figure
which could be a study for this woman
nude, and on either side of her studies
for the *Nude with Hands Crossed* (no.
31) in the Zacks collection. This close
relationship between certain works of
1905 and others produced at Gosol,
which Picasso presumably visited only
in 1906, makes one wish there were
evidence that he had been there in
1905 as Zervos originally surmised.

33 LA TOILETTE

1906 / Z I: 325 (1905)

oil on canvas, 59-1/2 x 39 in.,
151 x 99 cm.

signed 'Picasso' upper left

Studies: Z VI: 737, 880

Provenance: John Quinn, New York
until 1926; acquired by the museum
1926

Picasso Exhibitions: Hartford 1934,
no. 18; New York 1936, Seligmann
no. 29; Boston 1938, no. 4; New York
1939, MMA no. 57; Mexico 1944;
Denver 1945; New York 1947,
Knoedler no. 26; Toronto 1949, no. 3;
London 1960, Arts Council no. 29

lent by The Albright-Knox Art
Gallery, Buffalo

Picasso's drawings for this painting
show that he wanted to contrast the
free upward movement in the contours
of the nude woman at the left with the
earthbound solidity of her serving
maid on the right. He makes both so
unrelated to a particular space or time
and so suggestive of the figures on
Greek lekythoi or gravestones that this
masterpiece has always seemed in its
simplicity and its delicacy to be a
dream of an ideal classical past.

34 HEAD OF FERNANDE/
TETE DE FERNANDE

Paris, late 1905/Z I: 323

bronze, 14-1/4 in. high, 36 cm.

signed 'Picasso' bottom

lent from the Collection of
Joseph H. Hirshhorn

WOMAN WITH KERCHIEF (FERNANDE)/
FEMME AU MOUCHOIR DE TETE

35 WOMAN WITH KERCHIEF
(FERNANDE)/FEMME AU
MOUCHOIR DE TETE

Gosol 1906/Z I: 319

gouache and charcoal, 26 x 19-1/2 in.,
66 x 49.5 cm.

signed 'Picasso' lower right

Studies: Z VI: 754, 755, 756, 760, 802

Provenance: Valentine Dudensing,
New York; T. Catesby Jones, New
York; acquired by the museum 1947

Picasso Exhibitions: New York 1939,
MMA no. 62; New York 1947,
Knoedler no. 24; New York 1962,
Tribute, Knoedler no. 27

lent by The Virginia Museum of
Fine Arts
T. Catesby Jones Collection

Fernande has written how contented
Picasso was on their yearly visits to
Spain, the first of which was to Gosol,
in the Spanish Pyrenees near the French
border, in 1906. From this summer trip,
which was so crucial to his work,
Picasso fortunately kept a notebook
intact, which Douglas Cooper has
published as *Picasso: Carnet Catalan*
(Paris: Berggruen, 1958). In it are
studies of Fernande which Cooper
points out (p. 47) are clearly related to
this painting. Picasso, by using the
kerchief, was able to concentrate upon
Fernande's strong features which he
sharpened somewhat so that they give
the impression of a mysterious
melancholy mask.

If this head of Picasso's mistress
Fernande is really from late 1905, it
would seem that her character and
features must have had much to do
with the strengthening of Picasso's
style. In the boldness, compactness,
density and economy of this piece of
bronze, Picasso broke with the frailer
forms of his earlier Rose Period works.
Fernande herself seems a goddess,
beautiful and remote.

36 RECLINING NUDE (FERNANDE)/
NU COUCHE

Gosol 1906/Z I: 317

gouache, 18-5/8 x 24-1/8 in.,
47.2 x 61.2 cm.

signed 'Picasso' lower right

Provenance: Paul Guillaume, Paris,
1934; Mr. and Mrs. Michael Straight;
their gift to the museum 1954

lent by The Cleveland Museum of Art
gift of Mr. and Mrs. Michael Straight

The delicate nude body of this gouache
is not unlike the nude in Buffalo's
painting (no. 33) but the head which
surmounts it somewhat disturbingly is
the enigmatic mask Picasso had
developed from Fernande's face. The
body and head are held together
visually by the freely swinging contours
of the figure but the lack of real
relationship between them suggests a
dream – not of idyllic Greece but of the
kind of fantasy (if not the same form
of it) one finds in the work of Henri
Rousseau who had exhibited three
works at the Autumn Salon of 1905.

37 HEAD OF AN OLD MAN /
    TETE D'HOMME

1906 / Z I: 380 (1905)

bronze, 6-3/4 in. high, 17 cm.,
ed. by A. Vollard

signed 'Picasso' on side at bottom

lent from the Collection of
Joseph H. Hirshhorn

This old man seems very close to one Picasso drew at Gosol in 1906 (Z I:346; Z VI: 765, 769, 770, 772, 773) even though the cheekbones do not project as far beyond the contours of the head. Perhaps he was the old man about whom Fernande wrote (Olivier p. 116), 'Un vieil homme de quatre-vingt-dix ans, ancien contrebandier, voulait absolument le suivre à Paris. Vieillard farouche, d'une beauté étrange et sauvage, il avait, malgré son âge, gardé ses cheveux et des dents tout usées, mais fort blanches. Méchant, acariâtre avec tous, il ne retrouvait sa bonne humeur qu'auprès de Picasso, qui a fait de lui un dessin très ressemblant.' The curious surface of this bronze may have been intended to indicate the man's great age.

38 PORTRAIT OF LEO STEIN
Paris 1906 / Z I: 250 (1905)
gouache, 9-3/4 x 6-3/4 in.,
24.7 x 17 cm.
not signed or dated

Provenance: Leo and Gertrude Stein,
Paris; Miss Etta and Dr. Claribel Cone,
Baltimore; acquired by the museum
1950

Picasso Exhibitions: New York 1957,
MMA p. 29; Philadelphia 1958, no. 27

lent by The Baltimore Museum of Art
Cone Collection

Leo Stein was the first of the remarkable American family to become
interested in Picasso and in 1904 to buy
a painting by him. Something of the
intelligence and perception which
made Leo Stein appreciate Picasso's
work at this period, and also his
limitations, can be seen in this portrait
of him. It also seems to answer the
description Fernande (Olivier p. 101)
has given us of him the first time he
and Gertrude paid a surprise visit on
Picasso in his studio: 'Lui, l'air d'un
professeur, chauve, avec des lunettes
d'or. Longue barbe aux reflets roux,
l'oeil malin.' If it were actually painted,
as it is supposed to have been, after
Picasso's return to Paris from Gosol in
1906, it must have been deliberately
done in the earlier Rose Period style to
which Leo was most responsive. As
Picasso advanced into the *Demoiselles
d'Avignon* late in 1906, Leo became
disillusioned and no longer bought
Picasso's work. On the other hand,
that same autumn Picasso painted
Leo's sister Gertrude, who had the
intelligence to understand what he was
doing throughout his career, with a
forceful mask-like face which
anticipated Picasso's movement into
cubism (Metropolitan Museum of Art,
New York, Z I: 352).

STANDING NUDE/NU DUBOUT

WOMAN SEATED AND WOMAN
STANDING/DEUX FEMMES

NUDE STANDING IN PROFILE/
NU DEBOUT DE PROFIL

39 STANDING NUDE/NU DEBOUT

1906/Z VI: 645

pencil, 24-13/16 x 18-1/16 in.,
63 x 45.8 cm.

signed 'Picasso' lower left by artist
in 1937

Related Works: Z I: 357, 365; drawing
in the collection of Mr. and Mrs.
Richard S. Davis, Wayzata, Minnesota

Provenance: Leo Stein to c. 1937;
Pierre Matisse Gallery, New York
c. 1937-43; gift of Mrs. Murray S.
Danforth to the museum 1943

Picasso Exhibitions: Princeton 1949,
no. 8

lent by The Museum of Art, Rhode
Island School of Design

In the process of developing the
monumental bodies he was to use
in the *Two Nudes* in the G. David
Thompson Collection (Z I: 366) Picasso
seems to have begun with a soft,
voluptuous body in a pastel (Z I: 357)
and then made it crisper in this
rhythmic pencil drawing in the
exhibition. He introduced her into a
composition with a reclining figure in
the charcoal drawing in the Davis
Collection, which seems to have been a
prelude to several others of two
female figures, drawn with increasingly
sculptural hardness. One which shows
this figure reversed at the left (Z I:365)
is close to the finished painting.

In the fall of 1906 Picasso took the faces
he had evolved at Gosol (see nos. 35
and 36) and strengthened them to
something close to a primitive mask
and, to support those heads, he
developed a solid body like the staunch
and massive trunk of a tree. He gave
these women a femininity of gesture
and a gentleness of expression which
seems to belie their sculptural severity
and hierarchical poses. These drawings
best express their innate natural dignity,
Picasso's own growing assurance and
his increasing interest in the clarification of three dimensional forms. It
seems to illustrate Gertrude Stein's
statement, 'After that little by little his
drawing hardened, his line became
firmer, his color more vigorous, naturally he was no longer a boy, he was
a man.'

These drawings, like no. 41, are
related to the *Two Nudes* in the G.
David Thompson Collection (Z I: 366)
and lead into the *Demoiselles
d'Avignon* (no. 46).

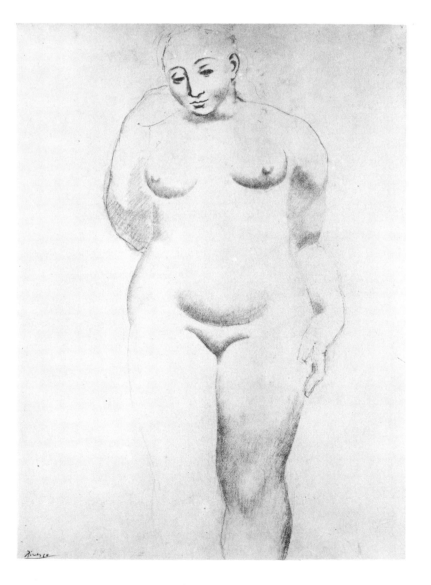

40 WOMAN SEATED AND WOMAN STANDING/DEUX FEMMES

late 1906/ Z I: 368

charcoal, 24-1/8 x 18-1/4 in., 61.2 x 46.3 cm.

signed 'Picasso' lower right

Related Works: Z I: 365, 369, 366; Z II: 594, 597, 649; Z VI: 911

Picasso Exhibitions: New York 1957, MMA p. 30; Philadelphia 1958, no. 35

lent by The Philadelphia Museum of Art
Louise and Walter Arensberg Collection
To be exhibited in Toronto only

41 NUDE STANDING IN PROFILE/ NU DEBOUT DE PROFIL

Paris 1906/ Z I: 369

charcoal, 21-1/16 x 14-3/16 in., 53.5 x 36 cm.

signed 'Picasso' lower right in red crayon

Related Works: Z I: 365, 366, 368

Provenance: A. Drouant, Paris; Ernest Brown & Phillips Ltd.; The Leicester Galleries, London; Arthur Wiesenberger; his gift to the museum 1943

lent by The Brooklyn Museum gift of Mr. Arthur Wiesenberger

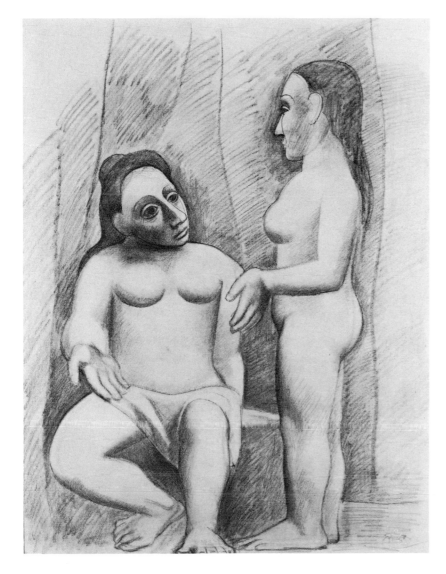

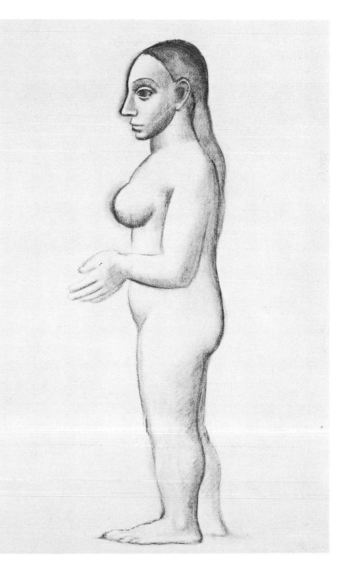

THE FLOWER VENDORS/PAYSANS

FLOWER GIRL/PAYSAN

SELF-PORTRAIT/AUTOPORTRAIT

42 THE FLOWER VENDORS/PAYSANS
1906/Z I: 311

ink and watercolour,
24-3/4 x 18-1/4 in., 62.8 x 46.3 cm.

signed 'Picasso' lower right

Related Works: Z I: 312, 384; no. 43

Provenance: Frank Perls Gallery,
Beverly Hills

Picasso Exhibitions: New York 1957,
MMA p. 28; Philadelphia 1958, no. 34

lent from the Collection of
Ayala and Sam Zacks

These two drawings are studies for
the painting in the collection of the
Barnes Foundation (Z I: 384), which
Barr (p. 48) has written, 'is particularly
important because more than any
previous Picasso it looks forward to
Cubism both in its free deformation
of natural forms and its flickering
angular planes which tend to spread
throughout the whole canvas thereby
creating an all-over unity of design.'
The Zacks drawing is more restrained
and more closely related to something
Picasso could have seen at Gosol;
it is also more tenderly human in
feeling. The Museum of Modern Art
Flower Girl is closer to Cubism in 'its
free deformation of natural forms.'

Picasso had painted many exploratory
portraits of himself before 1906; some
were comic, some sad, some filled with
a disturbing intensity. This self-portrait,
which is the largest he has ever done,
is related to the mask-like images he
had used for his portrait of *Gertrude
Stein* (The Metropolitan Museum of
Art, Z I: 352) and for his *Two Nudes*
(Z I: 366) after his return from Gosol
in 1906. In the clarification of the forms,
the solidity of the figure, the disciplined
energy of the contours, one feels a
strength and steadiness of purpose
which, when combined with the vision-
ary quality one sees in his eyes, could
explain Picasso's ability that winter to
produce his revolutionary masterpiece,
the *Demoiselles d'Avignon.*

43 FLOWER GIRL / PAYSAN

1906 / not in Z

pen and ink, 24-7/8 x 19 in.,
63.1 x 48.2 cm.

signed 'Picasso' lower left in pencil

Related Works: Z I: 311, 312, 384

Provenance: Mrs. Stanley B. Resor;
acquired by the museum 1950

Picasso Exhibitions: New York 1957,
MMA (addenda); New York 1962,
MMA

lent by The Museum of Modern Art,
New York
gift of Mrs. Stanley B. Resor

44 SELF-PORTRAIT / AUTOPORTRAIT

Paris 1906 / Z I: 375

oil on canvas, 36-1/2 x 28-3/4 in.,
92.6 x 72.9 cm.

signed 'Picasso / 1906' lower left

Studies: Z VI: 921

Provenance: A. E. Gallatin, his gift
to the museum

Picasso Exhibitions: Hartford 1934,
no. 20; Paris 1955, Décoratifs no. 11;
New York 1957, MMA p. 29;
Philadelphia 1958, no. 41

lent by The Philadelphia Museum
of Art
A. E. Gallatin Collection

Paris 1907
bronze, 7-1/4 in. high, 18.4 cm.
lent from the Collection of
Joseph H. Hirshhorn

In the rhythm running through the asymmetrical features of this small bronze head, one is made conscious of Picasso, as the artist, giving these impassive features a mobility.

All of Picasso's energies the winter of 1906-07 went into painting one of the monuments of his career – the *Demoiselles d'Avignon*. Its name, which refers to a cabaret or house of prostitution on the Carrer d'Avinyo (Avignon Street) in Barcelona, was given the work later and not by the painter. It was partly because this work absorbed him so completely that Derain told the young German who was to become Picasso's dealer, Daniel-Henri Kahnweiler, that Picasso would someday hang himself behind it. It disturbed his friends as much as it preoccupied him; Leo Stein became disenchanted with Picasso because of it, Matisse angry at it, and Braque temporarily bewildered by it. Under any circumstances it is a disturbing work; as recently as 1953 Sir Kenneth Clark wrote *(The Nude,* New York: Pantheon Books, 1953, p. 361): 'The *Demoiselles d'Avignon* is the triumph of hate.'

One of the shocking things which Picasso had done was to destroy the classical beauty and serenity he had achieved for such a short period of time in Rose Period works like Buffalo's *La Toilette* (no. 33). The central figure in the *Demoiselles* may have her arms bent above her head somewhat like the nude at the left of the earlier painting, but not for the same logical reason and not with the same mild expression on her face; instead her distorted arms seem to pull her whole angular body upward around the haunted mask of her face. The figure on the left may be in somewhat the same position as the serving maid on the right of *La Toilette*, but her body is constructed of harsh angles, her head

is dark and strange, and an arm above her head prevents any visual resolution within the body itself. A comparison of her with the more nearly similar drawing from Brooklyn (no. 41) emphasizes the restlessness of her forms. Although all the figures have the same angularity, the same rigidity and are surmounted by rather wistful mask-like heads, the three faces on the left could have been developed from the Gosol type (nos. 35 and 36), with some memory perhaps of the bronze *Mask with the Broken Nose* (no. 16) but, as Barr (p. 56) pointed out, the two heads on the right were added after Picasso made his first visit to the African collection at the Trocadero in 1907. In any case all five figures give an impression of an alien and haunted civilization.

When Picasso first jotted down a sketch for the *Demoiselles* on paper, he may not have thought of Cézanne, whose paintings of *Bathers* influenced the final work, or even of a primitive world. The first drawing (Z II: 19) seemed ordinary enough – a sailor walking into a heavily draped room in which another sailor sits surrounded by five nude prostitutes. In another sketch (Z II: 20), the characters lost any identity while Picasso played with possible curvalinear movements through the contours of their bodies. He discarded the sailors and worked through many drawings into one in which the movements assume their final harsh angularity (Z II: 24). This interest in movement had not been unprecedented in his work; it had existed in the reclining figure of *Fernande* (no. 36) and in the studies

(nos. 42 and 43) for the *Composition with Oxen* (Z I: 384) but here it had become the compulsive dominating element in the painting, as if it were some primitive supernatural force which permits the *Demoiselles* no escape, no rest and no serenity. If Barr (p. 57) is correct and 'Picasso originally conceived the pictures as a kind of *momento mori*,' he realized his ambition by the reminder of the possibilities of a rosy pink *Inferno*.

spring 1907 / Z II: 18

oil on canvas, 96 x 92 in.,
243.6 x 233.6 cm.

not signed or dated

Studies: Z II: 19, 643, 645, 647, 650;
Z VI: 826, 827, 829, 831; Z II: 20;
Z VI: 981, 980; Z II: 632–642, 644,
13; Z VI: 959, 917; Z II: 14, 21;
Z VI: 987, 990; Z II: 22, 24;
Z VI: 971, 969, 968

Provenance: purchased by Jacques
Doucet from the artist about 1920;
Georges Salles, Paris; Jacques
Seligmann & Co., Inc., New York;
acquired by the museum
April 24, 1939

Picasso Exhibitions: New York 1937,
Seligmann no. 5; New York 1939,
MMA no. 71; New York 1955, MMA;
New York 1957, MMA p. 33; Phila-
delphia 1958, no. 39; London 1960,
Arts Council no. 34; New York 1962,
MMA

lent by The Museum of Modern Art,
New York
acquired through the Lillie P. Bliss
Bequest

1908/Z II: 103

oil on canvas, 59 x 39-1/2 in.,
149.8 x 100.3 cm.

signed 'Picasso' on the back

Studies: Z II: 101, 102; Z VI: 1024,
1025

Related Works: Z II: 45, 47, 66,
673–676; Z VI: 993; Z II: 104, 105,
106, 107, 108 (completed work)

Provenance: Kahnweiler Gallery,
Paris ca 1909-ca 1917; unknown
private collections in Germany and
Paris; Dr. Fritz Nathan, Zürich by
1958; acquired by the museum
October 1958

Picasso Exhibitions: Dresden 1914;
Boston 1959

lent by The Museum of Fine Arts,
Boston
Juliana Cheney Edwards Collection

After he had finished the *Demoiselles,*
Picasso transformed the figure which is
second from the left in that work into
the *Dance of the Veils* of 1907 which
is now in Leningrad. In 1908 he
reversed this figure, changed her
stance, made her heavier and more
muscular and in four large watercolour
and gouache drawings, studied ways
to thrust our eyes through the composition to give a sense of both three
dimensions and an action which is far
greater than any Picasso could have
conventionally described. He was
essentially doing what Cézanne had
done but he gave the forms an energy
they had never had in the earlier
painter's work. If this woman is contrasted with her prototype in the
Demoiselles, several things are
immediately apparent; she is more
impersonal, more sculptural and, in
the forceful contrast of forms in her
body, more active. Two other things
about her are important for the
development of analytical cubism.
One is that Picasso has twisted her
torso into a distortion which is unprecedented in the *Demoiselles* and
has done it to shove our eyes around
her body. The other is that at least one
point, the left knee, the distinction
between her body and the setting
is not precisely defined.

48 THE FARMER'S WIFE / LA FERMIERE

1908 / Z II: 91

oil on canvas, 32 x 25-3/4 in.,
81.2 x 65.3 cm.

signed 'Picasso' on the back

Studies: Z II: 92; Z VI: 1002, 1003,
1004, 1005, 1006, 1007, 1008,
1009

Provenance: Shchukine Collection;
State Museum of Modern Art,
Moscow; transferred to The
Hermitage 1930

Picasso Exhibitions: Paris 1954, la
Pensée française I, no. 23; London
1960, Arts Council no. 277

lent by The Hermitage Museum,
Leningrad

After having given his forms so much emotional power in the *Demoiselles d'Avignon,* Picasso seems to have subsided into the sober considerations of abstract and intellectual problems by 1908. Fernande (Olivier p. 148) tells us that, very much disturbed by the suicide of their drug-addicted German painter friend, Vighels, Picasso decided to go to the French countryside, which he normally disliked, to recover. He seems to have sought comfort from the rural life in painting, uncharacteristically, landscapes and the most disciplined of still lifes. Out of this French village, la Rue des Bois, on the edge of a forest, also grew the monumental painting of a peasant, *The Farmer's Wife,* whom Zervos provocatively tells us was a Mme Putnam.

In his crisp studies for this work Picasso studied the figure from every angle as if he were preparing for a piece of sculpture, apparently anticipating cutting into wood in the way he conceived the bold, flat planes of her skirt and mask. With an expression which is somewhat simple and bewildered, the Leningrad *Farmer's Wife* stands nobly as if all the strength of man's discipline over the soil were contained in her powerfully muscled arms.

49 THE DRYAD / NU DANS UN FORET

winter 1908 / Z II: 113

oil on canvas, 73 x 42-1/2 in.,
185.3 x 108 cm.

Studies: Z II: 112, 661

Provenance: Shchukine Collection;
State Museum of Modern Art,
Moscow; transferred to The
Hermitage 1934

Picasso Exhibitions: London 1960,
Arts Council no. 278

lent by The Hermitage Museum,
Leningrad

Out of the forest near la Rue de Bois
also came the great figure of *The
Dryad.* She was conceived just as
sculpturally as *The Farmer's Wife,* the
planes of her body as clear and bold,
but this three-dimensional quality is
also related to the forceful movement
of her body and of our eyes around
that body. In working from the one
preliminary sketch, Picasso eliminated
a companion for her and simplified
her face from a mask, suggestive of
African works, to a shape without
any associations.

Like *The Farmer's Wife, The Dryad*
represents a movement into analytical
cubism in its colours and in the
emphasis upon form; she is also one
step further in that direction in the
expansive, complicated movement she
provides for our eyes.

50 NUDE/NU

winter 1908-1909 / Z II: 109

oil on canvas, 39-1/4 x 31-3/4 in.,
99.6 x 80.6 cm.

signed 'Picasso' on the back

Provenance: Shchukine Collection;
State Museum of Modern Art,

Moscow; transferred to The
Hermitage 1934

Picasso Exhibitions: Paris 1954, la
Pensée française I, no. 38; London
1960, Arts Council no. 279

lent by The Hermitage Museum,
Leningrad

The primitive vitality which runs
through Boston's *Standing Figure*
(no. 47), *The Dryad* (no. 49) or even *The
Farmer's Wife* does not run through
this nude; instead she is quiet and her
figure perceived in a sequence of
smaller, almost unrelated areas. The
head is a simple shape with the features
superficial decorations on its surface;
the only break comes in the curious
wedge-shaped gash on the right cheek.
The hair is handled, as Cézanne might
almost have done it, with the heavy
accents of contours and shadows
leading our eyes backward and forward
around the brow. In the relationship of
the angle of the head to the angle of
the neck (reinforced by the hand)
there is a certain animation but it never
becomes forceful, partly because the
head seems too heavy and only
perilously balanced by the pathetically
fragile right arm.

Throughout the painting Picasso
leads our eyes tentatively from one
indistinct area to another, making us
conscious of the different angles from
which we may approach an object
(or a human being) and fusing these
into a human form which is still distinguishable from its environment.
Even in a figure like this, which is so
far removed from a conventional form
for the human body, the suggestion
of human feelings persists; there
is something pathetic about this
gracefully lethargic nude woman.

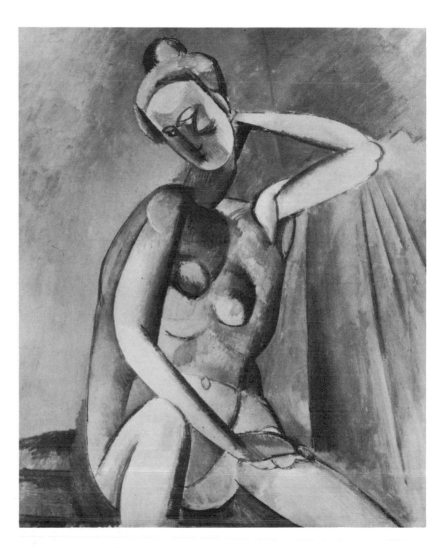

51 BUST OF A WOMAN/
BUSTE DE FEMME

spring 1909/Z II: 142

gouache, 25 x 19 in., 63.4 x 48.2 cm.

signed 'Picasso' upper right

Provenance: Ambroise Vollard, Paris;
Mrs. Stead-Ellis, Scotland; acquired by
present owners 1956

Picasso Exhibitions: London 1953,
Lefèvre no. 9

lent by Mr. and Mrs. Lazarus Phillips

Most cubist works of the spring of 1909
have a somewhat tentative character,
but this gouache does reveal Picasso
sharpening and strengthening the
features of the human face. He also
uses the straight brush strokes to direct
our eyes around the surfaces of the
figure. The bent head he so often uses
at this time makes us conscious of
the body's weight.

52 WOMAN WITH THE FAN/
    LA DAME A L'EVENTAIL

spring 1909/Z II: 137

oil on canvas, 40-3/8 x 32-3/8 in.,
102.5 x 82.1 cm.

Related Works: Z II: 144

Picasso Exhibitions: Milan 1953,
no. 338; Paris 1954, la Pensée
française I, no. 43

lent by The Pushkin State Museum
of Fine Arts, Moscow

The features of the face are so strongly
realized in this painting that they and
the way the woman slumps in her chair,
holds her left hand and wears her
clothes should identify the sitter as
something more than the *Woman with
the Fan.* At the same time this portrait
was one more formal problem in the
development of cubism. The woman's
face, although held together as a unit,
is made up of planes viewed from
different angles and from different
distances; the left eye, for example, is
further away from us than the right,
and the right nostril is seen from a
profile point of view while the mouth
is seen from the frontal. Our eyes may
shift over the face in this manner, but
those movements are very much
disciplined and contained. Around her
head the pleated jabot, the fan, the
hat, the vase, her garments produce
more complicated movements within
a limited plane, while still retaining
their own identities.

53 HEAD OF FERNANDE/
TETE DE FERNANDE

summer 1909/Z II: 573
bronze, 16-1/2 in. high, 41.9 cm.
The Art Gallery of Toronto

During the summer of 1909 at Horta de
San Juan, Picasso made many studies
of Fernande, apparently seeking some
solution for the human head which
would be more decisive than his
treatment of it, for example, in the
Leningrad *Nude* (no. 50). One of these
studies was this piece of sculpture
which was cast in bronze. Picasso still
kept the form of the head intact but he
broke into it with forceful gashes or
troughs which carry our eyes in varying,
interrupted directions around it. The
energetic sculptural quality these
produced can be seen by comparing
this bust with the earlier one of
Fernande (no. 34).

54 YOUNG WOMAN IN A CHAIR/
JEUNE FILLE DANS UN FAUTEUIL

late 1909/Z II: 215 (1910)

oil on canvas, 28-3/4 x 23-5/8 in.,
73 x 60 cm.

signed 'Picasso' upper right

Provenance: Mlle Pertuisot Collection

(Zervos); Paul Rosenberg, New York;
Alex L. Hillman, New York; gift to the
museum January 30, 1953

Picasso Exhibitions: New York
1962, MMA

lent by The Museum of Modern
Art, New York
gift of Mr. and Mrs. Alex L. Hillman

In the fall of 1909 (in paintings like this *Young Woman in a Chair*), Picasso benefited from the studies of Fernande that summer but went even further in breaking up the heads into shapes which no longer leave the features intact. The rough horizontals here are indefinite in form and seem to play against each other in space, rather than in relation to each other in developing a continuous three-dimensional surface. Picasso also went further than the Leningrad *Nude* (no. 50) in breaking the body apart and in emphasizing the separate identities of its arbitrarily designed components.

Although there are passages, like the serpentine movement between the arms and the light playing over those arms, which are satisfyingly beautiful in themselves, the principal purpose of the forms seems to be an expressive one. The head withdraws on the violently constructed cords of the neck. The cold gray of the shapeless bottom part of the face contrasts with the warmth of the rest of the painting and produces the most poignant effect of human anguish.

NUDE FIGURE/FEMME NUE

THE ROWER/LE RAMEUR

MAN WITH A PIPE/TETE AVEC PIPE

55 NUDE FIGURE/FEMME NUE
winter 1909/Z II: 194

oil on canvas, 38-1/2 x 30 in.,
97.7 x 76.1 cm.

not signed or dated

Provenance: Ambroise Vollard, Paris;

John Quinn, New York; Earl Horter,
Philadelphia; purchased by the
museum from Pierre Matisse Gallery
1954

Picasso Exhibitions: São Paulo 1954,
no. 3

lent by The Albright-Knox Art Gallery,
Buffalo

In the changes within analytical cubism,
this is one of the last to make clear
what Picasso insisted upon in an
interview with Zervos in 1935 (Barr
p. 273) 'There is no abstract art. You
must always start with something.
Afterward you can remove all traces of
reality. There's no danger then, anyway,
because the idea of the object will have
left an indelible mark. It is what started
the artist off, excited his ideas, and
stirred up his emotions. Ideas and
emotions will in the end be prisoners
in his work. Whatever they do, they
can't escape from the picture.' In this
picture there is something lighthearted
about this dancing figure in spite of the
elements in cubism which Rosenblum
(p. 67) describes as 'a rigorously
restricted and impersonal vocabulary
of simple geometric shapes' and a
'monkishly somber palette of ochers,
grays and browns.'

56

In Cadaqués where he lived with
Fernande and worked with Derain
the summer of 1910, Picasso's works
became as nearly non-objective (to
the spectator at least) as they were ever
to become. The existence of the rower
in this painting is, for example, almost
impossible to detect without the
assistance of the title. Picasso's use of
analytical cubism to provide an
equivalent for action probably reached
its purest form here.

57

This rare analytical cubist drawing
clarifies the masterful rhythm of lines –
contracting slightly to the right of the
centre here, expanding beyond it –
which underlies other analytical cubist
works. These lines produce a disciplined
scaffolding which contrasts with the
rough, varied and apparently spontaneous brush strokes of wash which
suggest the indefinite, constantly
changing space around it. From the
scarcity of such developed analytical
drawings one suspects that Picasso
must either have formulated the paintings completely in his mind first or
worked them out upon the canvases.

56 THE ROWER / LE RAMEUR

Cadaqués, summer 1910 / Z II: 231

oil on canvas, 28-3/8 x 23-3/8 in.,
72 x 59.3 cm.

signed 'Picasso' on the back

Provenance: Ambroise Vollard, Paris;
509 Gallery, New York; Earl Horter,
Philadelphia; Pierre Matisse Gallery,
New York

Picasso Exhibitions: New York 1962,
Tribute, Saidenberg no. 1

lent by Mr. and Mrs. Ralph F. Colin

57 MAN WITH A PIPE / TETE AVEC PIPE

Céret, summer 1911 / Z II: 280

charcoal and ink wash, probably oil,
25 x 18-1/4 in., 63.4 x 46.3 cm.

signed 'Picasso' lower left on the back

Related Works: Z II: 289

Provenance: Henri Kahnweiler; Alfred
Flechteim; J. Seligmann and Co.,

New York; acquired by the museum
1952

Picasso Exhibitions: New York 1952,
Valentin, no. 21; San Antonio 1954,
no. 16; Houston 1955, no. 12; New
York 1957, MMA p. 40; Philadelphia
1958, no. 57

lent by The Fogg Art Museum,
Harvard University

58 MA JOLIE
(Woman with a Zither or Guitar)

winter 1911-1912 / Z II: 244 (1911)

oil on canvas, 39-3/8 x 25-3/4 in.,
100 x 65.3 cm.

signed 'Picasso' on the back

Provenance: Marcel Fleischmann
Collection, Zürich; on loan from
M. Fleischmann to Museum of
Modern Art 1939-1946; purchased by
the museum December 17, 1946

Picasso Exhibitions: Zürich 1932,
no. 66; New York 1939, MMA no. 99;
New York 1941-42, MMA; New York
1955, MMA; Paris 1955, Décoratifs
no. 28; New York 1957, MMA p. 40;
Philadelphia 1958, no. 58; New York
1962, MMA

lent by The Museum of Modern Art,
New York
acquired through the Lillie P. Bliss
Bequest

As Cubism retreated further from the
world of appearances Braque and
Picasso found devices like the treble
clef and the letters 'Ma Jolie' here to
provide some conventional way for the
spectator to place himself in postion
and in scale in relation to the painting.
And as apparently abstract as a work
like this had become, Picasso would
still provide certain concrete facts like
the flat fingers of a hand on the lower
right or pairs of eyelashes to deflate
any possibility of our being completely
captivated by an abstract beauty.
Nevertheless that beauty, created by
the contractions in certain areas against
the freedom of others, by the movement along the lines and particularly
by the light, does exist even if it is
punctured occasionally by these
reminders of reality. Cubism had
always been dependent upon the play
from light to dark, and in Picasso's
work it frequently had the romantic
suggestions of Rembrandt's chiaroscuro;
in *Ma Jolie* it is largely disciplined
within the armature of the lines of the
painting but in the right hand corner it
opens up with rich strokes of paint
which suggest an indefinite, palpitating
light as open and radiant as a late
painting by Monet.

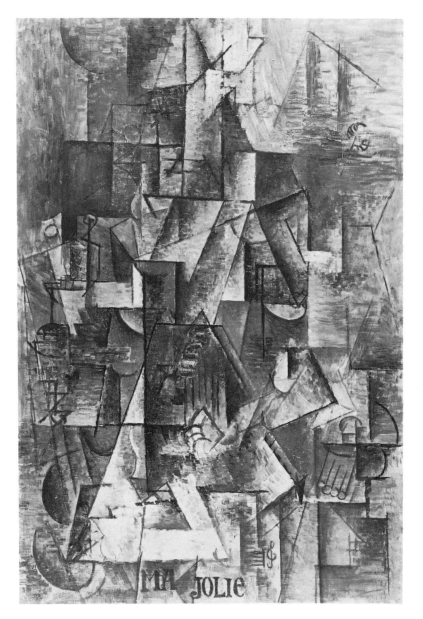

59 J'AIME EVA

1912 / Z II: 364

oil on canvas, 38-3/4 x 25 in.,
98.3 x 63.4 cm.

signed 'Picasso 1912' on the back

Provenance: Arthur B. Davies;
Ferargil Gallery; gift of Ferdinand
Howald, April 23, 1931

Picasso Exhibitions: New York 1939,
MMA no. 108

lent by The Columbus Gallery
of Fine Arts
the Ferdinand Howald Collection

This work was a gesture of love from
Picasso toward his new mistress, Marcel
Humbert (Eva), of whom he wrote to
Kahnweiler on June 12, 1912, 'I love her
very much and I shall write her name
on my pictures.' Here he wrote 'j'aime
Eva' as Penrose (p. 169) has said, 'like a
lover's inscription in the bark of a tree,'
and he composed the picture so that its
diagonals and arcs would lead our eyes
to it. As a tribute to this love, perhaps,
he brightened his colours, produced
longer more continuous lines to suggest
more static shapes which remain more
stably parallel to the picture plane.
He even gave the picture more of a
central core or trunk around which the
forms are assembled. The effect is
an analytical cubist work without
any somber undertones; it is almost
joyous.

60 MAN WITH A PIPE/TETE AVEC PIPE

1912 / Z VI: 1144

charcoal on paper, 24-1/2 x 18-1/2 in.,
62.2 x 47 cm.

signed 'Picasso' on the back

Provenance: unknown Swiss private
collector; Earl Stendhal, Los Angeles;
Curt Valentin; acquired by present
owners November 11, 1950

Picasso Exhibitions: Houston 1955,
no. 13; New York 1957, MMA p. 40;
Philadelphia 1958, no. 62

lent by Dr. and Mrs. Israel Rosen

Picasso was clarifying analytical cubism
in 1912, continuing and solidifying
lines, retaining pattern, giving even a
charcoal drawing like this one a
suggestion of colour quite apart from
the description of light and shadow,
in short turning analytical cubism into
a more decorative art form. And
curiously enough, perhaps because
analytical cubism had been so serious
and so restraining, humour for the first
time begins to appear in his work as it
does here in the hat, the moustache,
the mouth and even in his mockery
of the analytical cubist eyes.

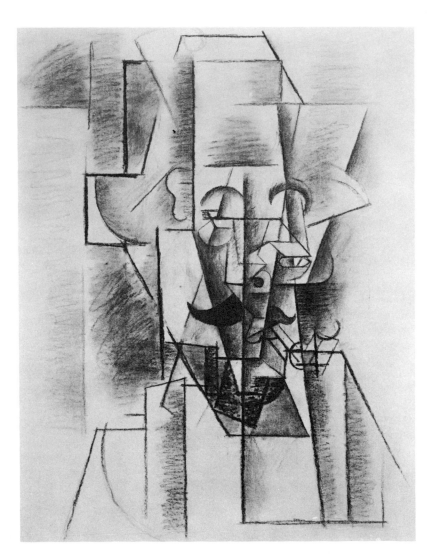

61 HEAD/TETE

1912/Z II: 403

collage, 18-1/2 x 11 in., 47 x 28 cm.

Provenance: Theodore Schempp,
Paris; acquired by present owner 1929

lent from the Collection of
Sidney Janis

In 1912 Picasso made the first collage
and that same year Braque began to
make pictures of pasted paper which
are called papier collés. Picasso, like
Braque, became interested in drawing
over even such simple pasted papers
as newsprint, although his results
were rarely as serenely decorative as
Braque's; his papier collés tended to
become animate, even rather human,
shapes. He was actually developing a
vocabulary for the human head – the
shape of the ears which he had derived
from Iberian sculpture in 1906, two
dots for eyes and a straight line below
an arch to represent the brows and
nose. And often he would pun, as he
did here, in making the right side of
the head like the side of a guitar.

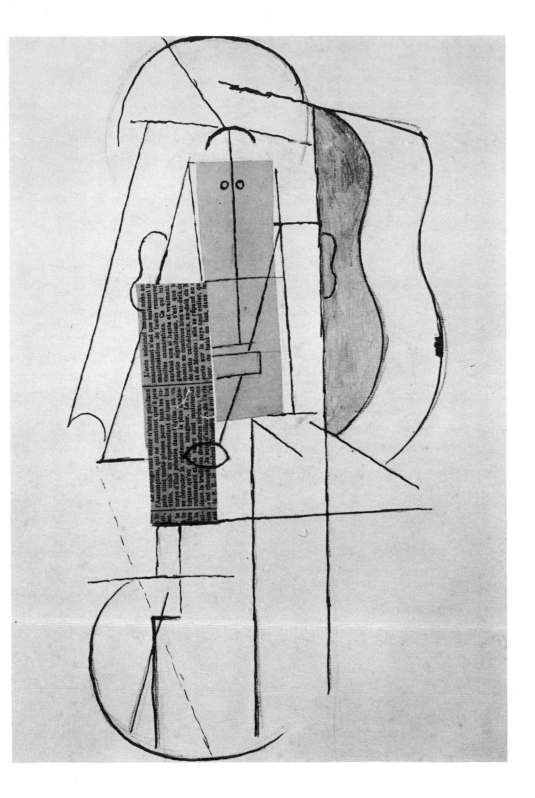

62 HEAD OF A MAN / TETE D'HOMME

spring 1913 / Z II: 431

oil, charcoal, ink and pencil on sized paper, 24-1/4 x 18-1/4 in., 61.5 x 46.3 cm.

signed 'Picasso' upper left later

Related Works: Z II: 425, 426, 427; Jardot no. 33

Provenance: Roger Fry, London; Max-Pol Fouchet, Paris; acquired by present owner 1955

Picasso Exhibitions: London 1960, Arts Council no. 69; New York 1962, Tribute, Saidenberg no. 15

lent by Mr. Richard S. Zeisler

Some reminiscences of analytical cubism persist in a painting like this – in the shadows by some of the lines and the refusal to permit certain shapes, like the striped one, to continue as an unbroken surface. There are also more immediate echoes of collage in its imitation of coloured papers. The head's energy, however, comes from a new element – a vibrant use of brilliant colour which enlivens the movement of the composition back and forth like a pendulum.

63 THE HARLEQUIN/L'ARLEQUIN

Céret, summer 1913/Z II: 333

oil on canvas, 34-7/8 x 18-1/8 in.,
88.5 x 46 cm.

signed 'Picasso' later lower right
and 'Picasso' on the back

Related Works: Z II: 326, 325, 328;
Z VI: 1774

Provenance: Alphonse Kann, Paris;
Galerie Rosengart, Lucerne (1955);
acquired by the museum 1956

Picasso Exhibitions: Paris 1955,
Décoratifs no. 39; London 1960, Arts
Council no. 71; Bremen 1961, no. 4

lent by the Gemeentemuseum,
The Hague

In paintings like this which unquestionably belong to the new period called *Synthetic Cubism*, the influence of Picasso's papier collés can be seen in the flatter rectangular planes and in the subtle play with texture and colour. Besides being more decorative (and lighthearted) than analytical cubism, synthetic cubism did represent a different point of view which, as Mr. Golding points out (see essay), Picasso's compatriot, Juan Gris, a painter who came to cubism in the footsteps of Braque and Picasso, summed up by saying, 'Cézanne turns a bottle into a cylinder, but . . . I make a bottle — a particular bottle out of a cylinder.' In analytical cubism Picasso, like Cézanne, had turned his bottles (or human beings) into many roughly geometric shapes. With synthetic cubism he, like Juan Gris, joyously turned the geometric forms into something which magically comes alive like this wistful, wacky harlequin.

64 MAN SEATED AT A TABLE/
HOMME ACCOUDE SUR UNE TABLE

1914 / Z II: 506

pencil, 13 x 10 in., 33 x 25.4 cm.

signed 'Picasso/14' lower left

Provenance: John S. Newberry;
his gift to the museum 1960

Picasso Exhibitions: Princeton 1949,
no. 18; New York 1962, MMA; Toronto
1949, no. 43

lent by The Museum of Modern Art,
New York
the John S. Newberry Collection

This drawing shows the regard Picasso
felt for mass and weight and perspective – and even human weariness –
underneath his synthetic cubist forms.
In the hat, the head and the left sleeve
one can see the cubist forms emerging.

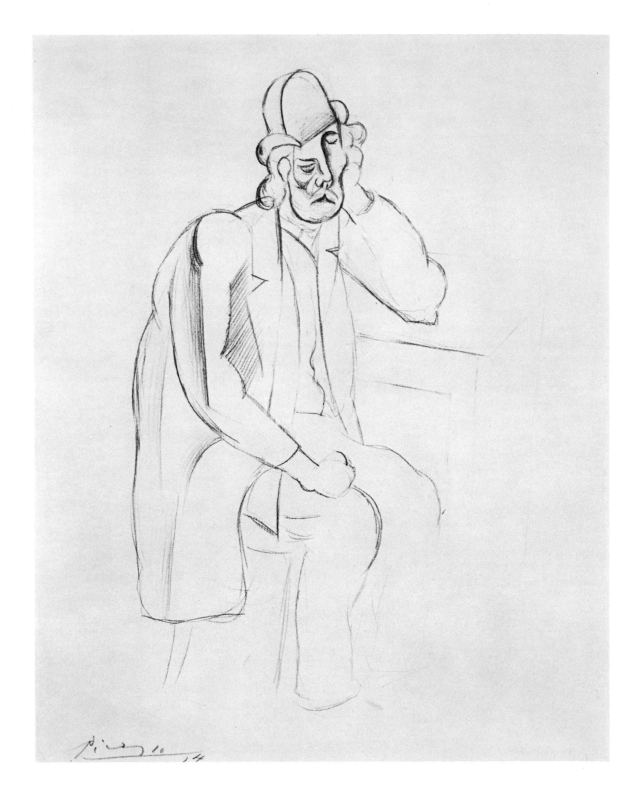

65 THE CARD PLAYER/
JOUEUR DE CARTES

Paris, winter 1913-14 / Z II: 466

oil on canvas, 42-1/2 x 35-1/4 in.,
107.9 x 89.5 cm.

not signed or dated

Related Works: Z VI: 1234

Provenance: Paul Guillaume, Paris;
Dr. G. F. Reber, Lausanne; Francis B.
Cooke, London 1939; purchased by
the museum through Dr. Paul Drey,

Picasso Exhibitions: Münich 1923,
Thannhauser; London 1939, no. 21;
Lyon 1953, no. 33; Milan 1953, no. 31;
Philadelphia 1958, no. 72; New York
1962, MMA

lent by The Museum of Modern Art,
New York
acquired through the Lillie P. Bliss
Bequest

As Picasso moved into synthetic cubism
his work, like *The Card Player,* became
increasingly decorative, playful and
colourful. Nevertheless in spite of the
keystone frieze, the palmette-orna-
mented panel, the wood graining, the
sequins and the playing cards, the
'JOI' which Picasso spells out in the
middle of the work seems decidedly
superficial. Under the skill and the
jokes there is less *joie de vivre* than an
underlying element of strangeness and
melancholy which humour cannot
explain or disguise.

Both the comedy and the strangeness
of many synthetic cubist works are
found in the monumental *Harlequin*
which belongs to what Barr (p. 93)
calls the Classic Period of Cubism. In
this painting Picasso exploited the
decorative possibilities of a harlequin's
suit for typical synthetic cubist pur-
poses but he also exploited its diamond-
shaped pattern to make the legs seem
to buckle a little under the figure.
This touch of the comic is almost lost,
however, in the suggestion of terror
communicated through the black
background, the strange white shape
with an eye against it, and the constant,
uncanny shifting of all the rigid forms.

1915/Z II: 555

oil on canvas, 72-1/4 x 41-3/8 in.,
183.4 x 105 cm.

signed 'Picasso 1915' lower right

Related Works: Z II: 554-559; Z VI:
1328, 1332, 1333, 1334

Provenance: artist to Léonce Rosenberg; Alphonse Kann collection,
Paris; Paul Rosenberg, New York;
purchased by the museum January 27,
1950

Picasso Exhibitions: Paris 1932, no. 99;
New York 1939, MMA no.126; New
York 1955, MMA; New York 1957,
MMA p. 47; Philadelphia 1958, no. 77;
London 1960, Arts Council no. 84;
New York 1962, MMA

lent by The Museum of Modern Art,
New York
acquired through the Lillie P. Bliss
Bequest

67 PIERROT

1918 / Z III: 137

oil on canvas, 36-1/2 x 28-3/4 in.,
92.6 x 73 cm.

signed 'Picasso/18' lower left

Related Works: Z III: 13, 126-130;
G 55

Provenance: Bourgeois Gallery, New
York; purchased by Sam A. Lewisohn

May 1923; bequest to the museum
January 22, 1952

Picasso Exhibitions: Paris 1932,
no. 108; New York 1939, MMA no. 139;
Paris 1955, Décoratifs no. 47; Münich
1955; New York 1962, MMA

lent by The Museum of Modern Art,
New York
Sam A. Lewisohn Bequest

Although sporadically from 1901 Picasso
had drawn, painted, etched and
modelled figures who had their basis
in the Commedia del Arte – particularly
pierrots and harlequins – it seems to
have been only in 1917, with his trip to
Italy together with Cocteau to work for
Diaghilev's company, that he realized
their original meanings.

For the first time Harlequin, for
example, became for Picasso a rather
raucous comedian with a stick (Z III:
10, 22, 30; Z VI: 1323). He was also
more conscious of the actors in their
costumes and began to make a distinction between the man who performed
the harlequin or the clown and what he
wore. In this picture, which represents
the return to a more conventional way
of painting, Picasso gives us a sad
Pierrot – but one who is unhappy as a
man, rather than inherently so as a
clown.

PORTRAIT OF LEOPOLD ZBOROWSKI

TWO BALLET DANCERS/
DEUX DANSEUSES

WOMAN WITH A PITCHER /
FEMME TENANT UN VASE

68 PORTRAIT OF LEOPOLD
ZBOROWSKI
Paris 1919 / not in Z
pencil, 8-5/8 x 7-1/4 in.,
21.8 x 18.3 cm.
signed 'Picasso' lower right

Provenance: Miss Etta and Dr. Claribel
Cone; bequeathed to the museum
1950

lent by The Baltimore Museum of Art
Cone Collection

In 1919 Picasso seems to have become
preoccupied with dense, sculptural
form, perhaps as a reaction to the
relative flatness of synthetic cubism.
In this head of Leopold Zborowski,
Picasso emphasized the strong skull
and used the beard to model it further.
His image of this Polish poet is considerably heavier than that of the
Italian painter, Modigliani (1884-1920),
for whom Zborowski was both a dealer
and a friend. Picasso and Modigliani
only agree upon the small eyes and
softly formed mouth. Douglas Cooper
in the *Baltimore Museum of Art News*
(June 1958, vol. XXI, no. 5) writes about
having shown Picasso a photograph of
the drawing: *"He was delighted to see
it, confirmed, as I had always thought,
that it was Zborowski, and said that it
was the only true likeness of the man
and that he had done the drawing with
that purpose in mind . . . 'C'est exacte-
ment comme ça qu'il était,' he said,
'Je l'ai fait exprès pour que l'on voit.'"*

69

Picasso's interest in the ballet had begun in 1917 when he had accompanied
Jean Cocteau to Rome to do the sets
and costumes for Diaghilev's production of *Parade*. It continued with his
marriage to one of the minor members
of Diaghilev's company, Olga Koklova,
in 1918 and with his designs for *Le
Tricorne* which was produced for the
first time in London in 1919. It was on
that trip that he made this drawing
which, in spite of the stylization of the
lines, has an earthliness not unrelated
to the drawing of Zborowski.

70

This strong drawing was inspired by a
photograph and probably by an idea
for the ballet (perhaps for *Pulcinella*
for which Picasso made some magnificent drawings of Neopolitan fisher-
women – Z III: 243-246) but Picasso
seems to have been so absorbed in
the personality of this woman that
his drawing style became completely
unselfconscious. Although very much a
particular woman, this peasant, holding
the jug, has a dignity and monumentality which anticipates the goddesses
Picasso was to paint in the early
twenties. Indeed there is a link between
her and them in a painting of an Italian
woman of 1919 (Z III: 363).

69 TWO BALLET DANCERS/
DEUX DANSEUSES

London 1919/not in Z

pencil, 12-1/8 x 9-3/8 in.,
30.7 x 23.8 cm.

signed 'Picasso/Londres 19' lower left

Related Works: Z III: 338-345

Provenance: acquired by the museum
1963

lent by The Museum of Modern Art,
New York
the John S. Newberry Collection

70 WOMAN WITH A PITCHER/
FEMME TENANT UN VASE

1919 / Z III: 359

pencil, 25-7/8 x 19-5/16 in.,
65.6 x 49 cm.

signed 'Picasso/19' lower right

Provenance: Wright S. Ludington;
his gift to the museum 1946

Picasso Exhibitions: San Antonio 1954,
no. 24; Houston 1955, no. 17; Los
Angeles 1961, UCLA no. 76; New York
1962, Tribute, Duveen no. 2

lent by The Santa Barbara Museum of
Art
gift of Wright S. Ludington

71 ITALIAN PEASANTS/
PAYSANS ITALIENS

Paris 1919 / Z III: 431

pencil, 25-3/16 x 20-1/2 in.,
64 x 52 cm.

signed 'Picasso/19' lower left

Provenance: Wright S. Ludington;
his gift to the museum 1946

Picasso Exhibitions: San Antonio 1954,
no. 23; Houston 1955, no. 16; New
York 1957, MMA p. 49; Philadelphia
1958, no. 86; Los Angeles 1961, UCLA
no. 77

lent by The Santa Barbara Museum of
Art
gift of Wright S. Ludington

One form Picasso's desire for realism
took in 1919 was the copying of photographs. This accounts for the curious
cast of characters, among them the
arthritic Renoir (Z III: 413), who
suddenly appear in his drawings. A
photograph of these Italian peasants
probably attracted him because,
through his new interest in designing
for the ballet, he found the contrast
between the uniform and the peasant
costume a picturesque one. Although
Picasso did not disguise the photographic source for the drawing he
did use the draughtsman's conventions
of exaggeratedly strong lines and clean
cross-hatching to contradict any
photographic illusion.

The effects of Picasso's trip to Italy in
1917 had certain parallels with the
effects of Renoir's trip there in 1881,
and since he made drawings from
Renoir in 1918 and 1919 (Z III: 122,
413, 428-430) Picasso may not have
been unconscious of the similarities.
Italy aroused in him, as it had in
Renoir, a respect for ancient art, for
Raphael and above all for Ingres. The
firm, sensual body of the woman in this
Sleeping Peasants, for example, recalls
Ingres, particularly his *Turkish Bath.*

   The subject matter and the realism of
his work after that Italian trip suggest
that Picasso must have felt that, after
the rarified regions of Cubism, he must
like an Antaeus come in contact with
the soil. And this small painting
symbolizes the closeness of man to the
earth. At the same time cubism is not
forgotten as, within the narrow plane of
the figures, Picasso plays with the
foreshortening and scale of the limbs
and uses the lines of the hatching, as
well as the contours, to drive our eyes
through space in a movement which is,
however, much more sensual, more
continuous and more resolved than
anything cubism provided.

72 SLEEPING PEASANTS/LA SIESTE

1919/ Z III: 371

gouache, 12-1/4 x 19-1/4 in.,
31 x 48.8 cm.

signed 'Picasso/19' lower right

Studies: Z III: 369

Related Works: Z III: 368, 370, 372;
Z IV: 235

Provenance: John Quinn, New York;
Paul Rosenberg, Paris; Fukishima,
Japan; Mme Bélin, Paris; Paul
Rosenberg, New York; acquired by
the museum May 24, 1951

Picasso Exhibitions: Hartford 1934,
no. 33; New York 1957, MMA p. 49;
Philadelphia 1958, no. 83; New York
1962, MMA

lent by The Museum of Modern Art,
New York
Mrs. John D. Rockefeller, Jr. Fund

73 TWO NUDES / DEUX FEMMES

April 1920 / Z VI: 1404

mixed media on paper, 19 x 24-3/4 in., 48.2 x 62.8 cm.

signed 'Picasso' lower right

Related Works: Z IV: 55, 56, 58, 201, 202, 224

Provenance: Galerie Rosengart, Lucerne: acquired by present owners August 14, 1956

lent from the Collection of Ayala and Sam Zacks

In 1920 Picasso turned to the female nude and in one series painted a figure standing by another seated, with their limbs forming a pattern as involved and as active as a piece of Hellenistic sculpture. In the first conception of it, dated April 18th, (Z IV: 56) and in the collection of Douglas Cooper, contour lines describe the prettily rounded bodies and a piece of opalescent drapery covers the pelvic area of the figure on the left. The version in the exhibition in the degree of its abstraction and in the relative severity of the treatment of the body on the left, seems just preliminary to the one in a New York private collection (Z IV: 58) which is dated April 28th. In October Picasso continued with the idea but pulled and twisted the figures so that they seem angular giantesses anticipating those he has painted in the last decade. Finally on April 8, 1921 they appear in semi-cubist form (Z IV: 224).

After his marriage in 1918, Picasso seemed ready to express an uninhibited and pagan enjoyment of the sea. It appeared first in the decorations he made for the villa of Madame Errazuriz at Biarritz the summer of 1918 (Z III: 227) but it dominated most of the work Picasso did at Juan-les-Pins the summer of 1920. He peopled the water and the shore of his drawings and paintings with beautiful and indolent nude women. The sea is an inviting blue, the sand washed with golden light and the skin of the bathers a delicate pink. There is an underlying realism and humour to give the fantasy some strength; it can be seen in this pastel in the different heads of hair and in the concentration on the face of the bather at the left. Picasso loved to play optical games in space with the bodies although the effect is much looser and freer (perhaps to admit the sea) than it had been in his earlier work.

74 FOUR BATHERS/
    QUATRE BAIGNEUSES
    Juan-les-Pins, summer 1920/Z IV: 172
    pastel, 19 x 25 in., 48.2 x 63.4 cm.
    signed 'Picasso' lower left

Related Works: Z III: 227; Z IV: 161,
163-167, 169, 170, 173; Z VI: 1386,
1387, 1403

Provenance: Mme Marie Cuttoli,
Paris; acquired by Knoedler July 1962

lent by M. Knoedler

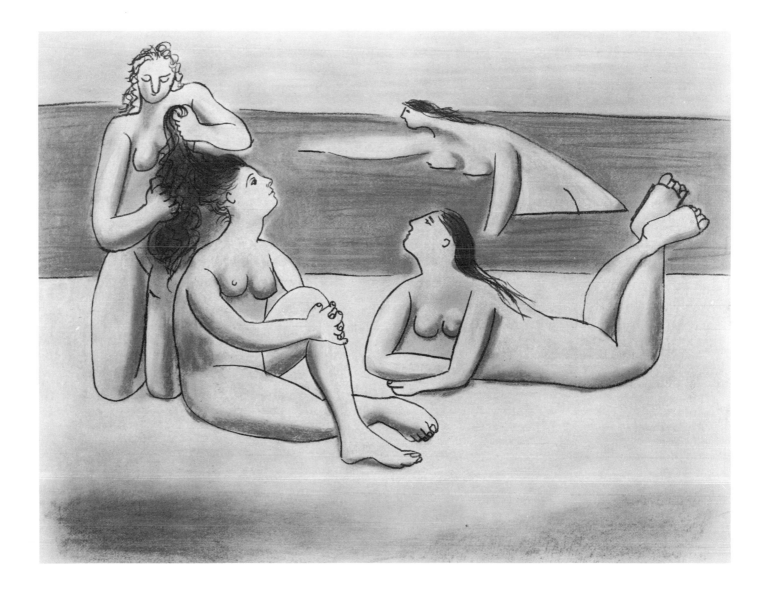

75 NESSUS AND DEJANIRA/LE RAPT

Juan-les-Pins, September 12, 1920/
Z VI: 1394

pencil, 8-1/4 x 10-1/4 in., 21 x 26 cm.

signed '12-9-20/Picasso' upper left

Related Works: Z IV: 184, 185, 187;
Z VI: 1395, 1402

Provenance: acquired by the museum
1952

Picasso Exhibitions: New York 1957,

MMA p. 51; Philadelphia 1958, no. 93;
New York 1962, MMA

lent by The Museum of Modern Art,
New York
acquired through the Lillie P. Bliss
Bequest

It is tempting to speculate that during his vacation the summer of 1920 at Juan-les-Pins, Picasso was made conscious by the sea of the ancient Mediterranean world and began to read classical mythology, and in particular the chthonic myths about creation and the fertility of the earth. Perhaps he even read Ovid's account *(Metamorphoses* book 9) of the centaur Nessus who loved Herakles' bride Dejanira and, when he was to carry her across a rain-swollen river, used the occasion to ravage her.

Picasso's first drawing of this subject on September 11, 1920 (Z IV: 185) shows a greater evidence of a frivolous, if robust, humour than of classical study. Three days later, however, his drawings (Z IV: 184, 187), like this one in the exhibition, became more serious even if the river Evenus is calm, Nessus leering and Dejanira acrobatic. On the fourteenth (Z VI: 1402) he turned to silverpoint which suggests Picasso thought the subject important enough for this difficult medium which in itself has associations with the past. In his one drawing that day he made Dejanira 'pale and trembling', and he gave Nessus' face a tenderness which shows his love. Finally (Z VI: 1395) on the twenty-second he made another silverpoint drawing in which Nessus is joyous and Dejanira desperate and both seem as inevitable as an ancient fertility rite.

76 THE RAPE/LE RAPT

1920/Z IV: 109

tempera on wood, 9-3/8 x 12-7/8 in.,
23.7 x 32.6 cm.

signed 'Picasso/1920' lower left

Studies: Z IV: 108

Provenance: Wildenstein & Co., Inc.,
New York; Philip L. Goodwin, New
York, December 1930-October 29,
1956

Picasso Exhibitions: Hartford 1934,
no. 38; New York 1939, MMA no. 150;
Mexico 1944; New York 1957, MMA
p. 55; Philadelphia 1958, no. 91;

London 1960, Arts Council no. 95;
New York 1962, MMA

lent by The Museum of Modern Art,
New York
the Philip L. Goodwin Collection

This tiny painting has many provocative echoes of the past. Is Picasso actually illustrating a particular Greek myth, perhaps one of those which symbolizes the rebirth of spring? Has he, in painting the dying warrior, thought of those from Aegina, from the Siphnian Treasury frieze at Delphi or upon the metopes of the Parthenon? In any case just as clearly as in the drawings of *Nessus and Dejanira* Picasso has withdrawn from a preoccupation with the minutiae of contemporary life into the classical world in which man's more basic nature could be revealed.

In spite of the suggestions of ancient Greece Picasso's figures are not classically proportioned. Although the forms of the bodies are continuous and the effect consistent he plays radically with their proportions, particularly when any foreshortening is involved. For the woman he had developed a body with enormous legs, large arms, a firm torso with small round breasts, and a small head; she also appears with almost the same features in a tiny painting in the Soby collection (Z IV: 309). In spite of these proportions she is, like the mammoth female figures of 1906 (see nos. 40 and 41), extraordinarily feminine and particularly tenderly so here, as she turns with a longing gesture toward her dying lover.

77 THE SPRING/LA SOURCE
Fontainebleau, July 18, 1921/Z IV: 301
pencil, 19 x 25-1/4 in., 48.2 x 64 cm.
signed 'Picasso/8-7-21' lower left
Related Works: Z IV: 302, 303, 304

Provenance: John S. Newberry;
acquired by the museum 1960
Picasso Exhibitions: Princeton 1949,
no. 25
lent by The Museum of Modern Art,
New York
the John S. Newberry Collection

It is possible that, since he was in rural France rather than at the sea the summer of 1921, Picasso thought nostalgically of the water. In allegorical form it became one of the principal themes of his work. He made smaller more energetic studies of *The Spring* before producing this larger serene drawing.

78 CLASSICAL HEAD / TETE CLASSIQUE

1921 ?/not in Z

crayon, 24 x 18-1/2 in., 61 x 47 cm.

signed 'Picasso' in ink lower left

Provenance: Paul Rosenberg, Paris;
stolen during World War II; regained
after a lawsuit by Paul Rosenberg;
acquired by present owners 1952

lent by Mr. and Mrs. David Meltzer

In the gentleness of the mouth and the
suggestion of her complete absorption
in something beyond herself, this
woman seems a maternal figure, related
perhaps to the great *Mother and Child*
of The Art Institute of Chicago (Z IV:
311) which Picasso painted in 1921.
Picasso's preoccupation with mother-
hood that year could perhaps have been
predictable since his first child, his son
Paul, had been born in February. This
head also has echoes in its forms of the
work of that great painter of maternities
of sixteenth century Italy, Raphael.

The name of Fontainebleau itself, where Picasso spent the summer of 1921, seems to have inspired his masterpiece of this period, the *Three Women at the Spring*. Many of his sketches for it were open and animated but he made the large painting quiet and enclosed. Although the painting itself and the colour are reminiscent of Roman work, the solid and solemn figures with their semitic faces seem to go back further into antiquity than the Greek and Roman world; their ritual at the spring could have been part of the oldest civilization between the Tigris and Euphrates rivers. The women themselves seem remote, in a trance, as if they themselves might be aware of an even more distant past.

That same summer and at the same place Picasso painted the two versions of his famous *Three Musicians* (The Museum of Modern Art, New York and The Philadelphia Museum of Art) which seem the antithesis of the classical *Three Women at the Spring* in form and in spirit. Actually this apparent ambivalence can be seen as early as 1915 when Picasso could paint a cubist *Harlequin* like no. 66 and make drawings as representational as his drawing of *Zborowski* (no. 68). Picasso himself gave a logical explanation for this seeming contradiction in his work; two years after that summer at Fontainebleau he said (Barr p. 271), 'Whenever I had something to say, I have said it in the manner in which I have felt it ought to be said. Different motives inevitably require different methods of expression.'

Although synthetic cubism and classical forms were used by Picasso to express quite different ideas they have something in common which differentiates them significantly from his earlier analytical cubist works, and that is that all these works are framed, organized around a central core and presented to the spectator with the conventional unity and completeness of a Renaissance picture. Both types seem to adhere to that quality which Baudelaire (C. Baudelaire, *The Mirror of Art,* ed. and trans. by J. Mayne, London: Phaidon, 1955, p. 120) felt to be characteristic of painting, 'Painting has but one point of view; it is exclusive and absolute,' an attitude which Picasso and Braque had actually made impossible with analytical cubism.

Picasso rarely has had any illusions about achieving the absolute, but at least in this period he was interested in the clarification and order which would make the absolute seem possible. When he wanted to make those forces which threaten man pictorially articulate, he expressed them in synthetic cubist forms. When he wanted to make those characteristics in man which endure explicit, he turned to the means which had been hallowed through the centuries as part of the tradition of classical art.

What did classicism mean to Picasso? It was certainly something alien to his Spanish Gothic imagination – but when it had attracted him first in 1905 and 1906 it had been because of its emphasis upon the freedom and the perfectability of man. It also seemed something he had come to know through Greek art, particularly those delicately painted jugs for oil, the lekythoi of the 5th century. In the twenties, when his interest in classicism was more enduring, it also seems to have been much broader – in literature as well as in the visual arts, in Rome as well as Greece, in the late manifestations of the classical spirit in the Renaissance and the 19th century as well as in antiquity itself. Although most of Picasso's classical works have, like this *Three Women at the spring,* considerable solemnity, there were others like the drawing of *Nessus and Dejanira* (no. 75) which have an enthusiastic pagan abandon. In all of them one feels that Picasso, in a state of relative contentment, could dream of this ideal stable world so far removed from his normal spiritual condition.

79 THREE WOMEN AT THE SPRING/ LA SOURCE

Fontainebleau, summer 1921/
Z IV: 322

oil on canvas, 80-1/4 x 68-1/2 in.,
203.7 x 174 cm.

signed 'Picasso/21' lower right

Studies: Z IV: 283, 284, 312-321, 323,
325, 326, 339, 340, 342, 344, 345, 346,
349, 356; Z VI: 1420, 1421; G 61, 64

Related Works: Z VI: 1397

Provenance: John Quinn, New York;
Meric Callery, Paris and New York;
J. B. Neumann, New York; Paul
Rosenberg, New York; Allan D. Emil,
New York; given to the museum
December 8, 1952

Picasso Exhibitions: Paris 1955,
Décoratifs no. 54; Oslo 1956, no. 52;
New York 1957, MMA addenda;
Philadelphia 1958, no. 99a; New York
1962, MMA

lent by The Museum of Modern Art,
New York
gift of Mr. and Mrs. Allan D. Emil

80 HEAD OF A WOMAN/
BUSTE DE FEMME

Dinard 1922/ Z IV: 393

oil on canvas, 39 x 31 in., 99 x 78.9 cm.

signed 'Picasso/22' upper left

Related Works: see no. 81

Provenance: Galerie Flechtheim,
Berlin 1930; Jules Furthman, Bel Air,
California; Theodore Schempp;
acquired by the museum 1941

Picasso Exhibitions: New York 1962,
Tribute, Duveen no. 21

lent by The Cincinnati Art Museum

In 1922 Picasso made his heads somewhat more delicate than they had been
the year before; even the hair curls up
more prettily. In that refinement there
are echoes of the features of the face
of his wife Olga who was probably no
longer so preoccupied with their child.
The faces, like this one, are often somewhat wistful and gently bewildered
without the complacent absorption of
a head like no. 78.

The manner in which Picasso handled
his oils as if it were an opaque medium,
modelled constantly with the shape of
his brushstrokes and painted with a
certain apparent spontaneity with
broken strokes, suggests the so-called
'Impressionism' of Roman painting
which he seems to have remembered
even five years after his visit to
Naples and Pompeii.

81 THE BATHER/NU

Dinard 1922/Z IV: 382

oil on panel, 7-3/8 x 5 in.,
18.7 x 12.6 cm.

signed 'Picasso/22' upper right

Studies: Z IV: 377

Related Works: Z IV: 359, 360, 381,
386, 394, 395

Provenance: Samuel Kootz, New
York; acquired by the museum 1931

Picasso Exhibitions: Hartford 1934,
no. 41; New York 1939, MMA no. 169;
Denver 1945; New York 1957, MMA
p. 55; Philadelphia 1958, no. 102;
New York 1962, Tribute, Duveen
no. 25

lent by The Wadsworth Atheneum,
Hartford, Connecticut
the Ella Gallup Sumner and Mary
Catlin Sumner Collection

This precious tiny painting is full of
apparent contradictions – the miniature
of a giantess – the heavy body which
might suggest Renoir if it were not so
completely lacking in sensuality – the
scale of that body which is nevertheless
completely dominated by the small and
pensive head. The gestures are even as
feminine as a Watteau's. It is finally a
work in which colour and light and
shadow also contribute to its dignity
and to its tenderness.

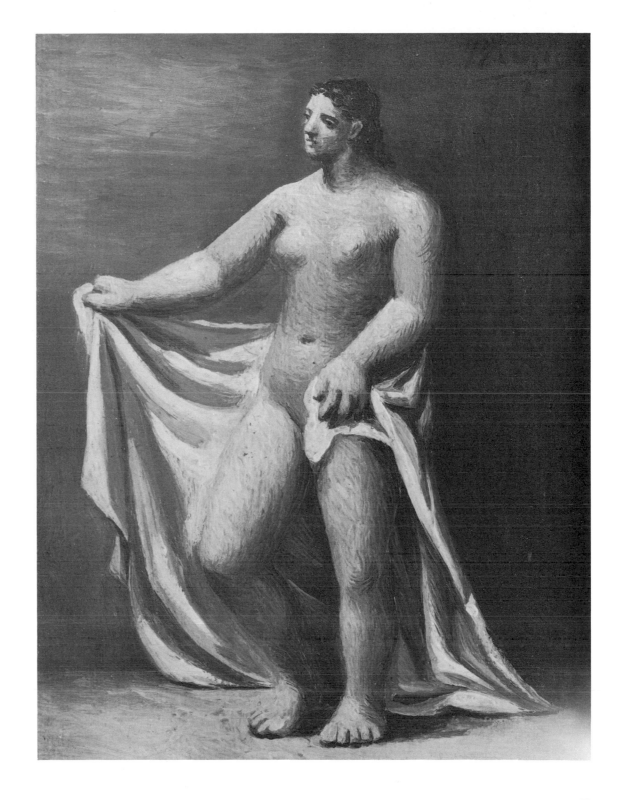

SEATED DANCER / DANSEUR ASSIS

THE SIGH / SALTIMBANQUE ASSIS

STUDY FOR THE PIPES OF PAN

82 SEATED DANCER / DANSEUR ASSIS
early 1923 / not in Z
pencil, 12-5/8 x 9-3/4 in., 32 x 24.7 cm.
not signed or dated
Related Works: Z V: 4-12

Provenance: Serge Diaghilev; willed
to Serge Lifar by Diaghilev 1929;
acquired by the museum 1933

lent by The Wadsworth Atheneum,
Hartford, Connecticut
the Ella Gallup Sumner and Mary
Catlin Sumner Collection

Picasso still continued to work for
the ballet and he may have seen this
restless young dancer at one of the
rehearsals the winter of 1922-23. He
drew him twisting in his chair from
several angles and in moods ranging
from boredom to unhappy doubt. He
wears the costume of a clown, but like
all of Picasso's clowns of this period
(Z V: 14, 15, 17, 23, 37, 131, 135), as if
it were fancy dress. This drawing, which
both Diaghilev and Lifar owned, is a
spirited simplification of one (Z V: 9)
Picasso had dated 1923.

83

The largest and probably the last of
these studies of the seated dancer in
the costume of a clown is this canvas
which Jean Cocteau told Picasso looked
as if it were 'painted in sighs.' Picasso
gave the work curiously literal narrative
suggestions including the panelling of
the wall, the rug and most obviously the
cane. Since the youth is slenderer and
more lethargic than any of the studies
of him, and the work is drawn and
painted with the most exquisite
refinement, it seems full of the kind of
nostalgia which caused Cocteau to
christen it *The Sigh*.

84

In 1923 Picasso made many drawings of
a tousled haired youth playing the Pipes
of Pan. Usually he played his pipes for
indolent, nude women or for pairs of
lovers, but Picasso finally subdued his
pose and placed him to the right of an
inert standing figure who resembles
Picasso himself; this painting is the
Pipes of Pan (Z V: 141) which Picasso
considered to be his major work of this
period and which he has kept in his
own collection. This charming drawing
of the youth alone reveals the changes
Picasso kept making as he worked
toward the final version, and the assurance with which he could bring the
drawing together with a few crisp,
black lines.

83 THE SIGH / SALTIMBANQUE ASSIS

early 1923 / Z V: 12

oil on charcoal on canvas,
23-3/4 x 19-3/4 in., 60.2 x 50 cm.

signed 'Picasso/23' lower right

Related Works: Z V: 4-11 and no. 82

Provenance: C. de Hauke;

M. Knoedler & Co., New York;
acquired by present owner 1931

Picasso Exhibitions: New York 1930,
Reinhardt no. 12; Hartford 1934,
no. 47; New York 1939, MMA no. 174;
Denver 1945; Princeton 1949. no. 28;
New York 1962, Tribute, Duveen
no. 36

lent by Mr. James Thrall Soby

84 STUDY FOR THE PIPES OF PAN

1923 / Not in Z

charcoal, 25-3/16 x 19-5/16 in.,
64 x 49 cm.

signed 'Picasso' in pen and ink lower
right

Related Works: Z V: 107-114, 117-125,
130, 141; Z VI: 1441, 1442, 1448

Provenance: acquired by the museum
1954

lent by The Art Institute of Chicago
bequest of Joseph Winterbotham

86 TORSO OF A WOMAN/

TORSE DE FEMME

1923 / Z V: 156

oil on canvas, 39-3/8 x 31-1/2 in.,
100 x 80 cm.

signed 'Picasso' lower right

Provenance: willed by M. Meunier to
the museum 1954

lent by the Musée National d'Art
Moderne, Paris

This torso of a woman in its conscious
classical beauty seems related to some
1923 sketches by Picasso, in which a boy
plays the pipes of Pan while a young
man holds up a mirror to a young
woman so that she may study her own
reflections there (Z V: 114, 118-125,
130).

87 THREE CLASSICAL FIGURES/
FEMME AU VOILE DEBOUT, DEUX
HOMMES ASSIS

1923-24 / Z V: 171

sanguine, 42 x 28-1/4 in.,
106.6 x 71.7 cm.

signed 'Picasso' upper right

Related Works: Z V: 169, 172

Provenance: Knoedler; acquired by
present owners 1938

Picasso Exhibitions: New York 1962,
Tribute, Duveen no. 37

lent by Mr. and Mrs. Hugh Chisholm

Picasso's pious neo-classicism may have
reached its epitome here. There seems
to be a respect for antiquity in the
subject matter, the proportions and the
purified representational style. At the
same time it is a work in which he
made space meaningful visually by the
movement along the contour lines,
(diagonally back to the standing figure
of the woman), and meaningful psychologically by the gaze between the
man and woman.

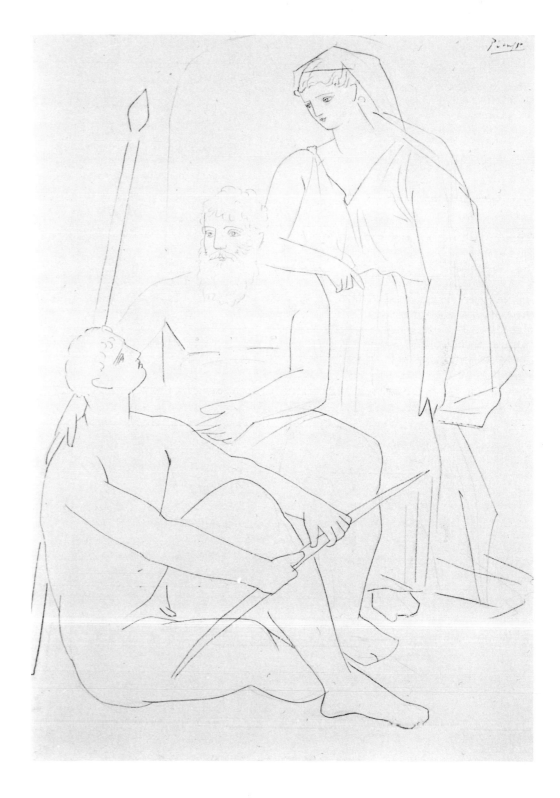

THREE FEMALE NUDES DANCING/
TROIS GRACES

THREE GRACES/TROIS GRACES

88

Picasso, who had etched groups of
three women the winter of 1922-23,
the next summer at Cap d'Antibes drew
them with considerably more abandon.
His handling of the pen was sure and
spontaneous and he made little
pleasantries like the sudden recession
of the leg on the right, or the surprise
the central figure shows at the hand
which is thrust up toward her.

89

This is so closely related to no. 88 and
to the drawings illustrated in Zervos,
that it is reasonable to assume that
they were all from a notebook in which
Picasso kept jotting down these joyful
nudes he might have imagined having
originally inhabited the Cap d'Antibes.
There is another not recorded by
Zervos in the collection of Vincent
Price; see Millier.

88 THREE FEMALE NUDES DANCING/
TROIS GRACES

Cap d'Antibes 1923/not in Z

pen and ink, 13-7/8 x 10-3/8 in.,
35.2 x 26.3 cm.

signed 'Picasso' lower right

Related Works: G 102-108;
Z V: 98-104; Z VI: 1434, 1436, 1445

Provenance: Edouard Jonas, Paris;
acquired by the museum 1952

lent by The National Gallery of
Canada, Ottawa

89 THREE GRACES/TROIS GRACES

Cap d'Antibes 1923/not in Z

pen and ink, 11 x 8-1/2 in. (sight),
28 x 21.5 cm.

signed 'Picasso' upper left

Related Works: G 102-108;
Z V: 98-104; Z VI: 1434, 1436, 1445

Provenance: Saidenberg Gallery,
New York

lent by Mr. M. F. Feheley

THREE DANCERS/TROIS DANSEURS

FOUR BALLET DANCERS/
QUATRE DANSEUSES

90   THREE DANCERS/TROIS DANSEURS

Monte Carlo 1925 / Z V: 437

pen and ink, 13-5/8 x 9-3/4 in. (sight),
34.5 x 24.7 cm.

signed 'Picasso/25' upper right

Related Works: Z V: 427-436, 438

Provenance: Miss Etta and
Dr. Claribel Cone, Baltimore;
bequeathed to the museum 1950

lent by The Baltimore Museum of Art
Cone Collection

91   FOUR BALLET DANCERS/
QUATRE DANSEUSES

Monte Carlo 1925 / Z V: 422

pen and ink, 13-7/8 x 10 in.,
35.2 x 25.3 cm.

signed 'Picasso/25' lower right

Related Works: Z V: 417-420, 423

Provenance: acquired by the museum
1935

lent by The Museum of Modern Art,
New York
gift of Mrs. John D. Rockefeller, Jr.

90

In 1925 Picasso must have kept a notebook as he had done at Cap d'Antibes
two years before – but this time he was
working from life, from the dancers
of Diaghilev's company. His line is,
therefore, very slightly more rounded
and somewhat more solid. The sense
of fluid movement through space is
very strong, enhanced by the variations
in the width of the line as much as
by the direction of it.

91

The effect of the purity of the line and
the compact classical composition in
this drawing is strong enough to
distract us from the extreme distortions
like the right leg of the male dancer –
or even the degree to which the whole
group is thrust back into space. The
female dancer on the right has the wild
intensity of a maenad which should
not leave us as surprised, as we usually
are, that the same year Picasso made
drawings like this, he painted the
disturbing *Three Dancers* (Z V: 426)
which he has kept in his own
collection.

SEATED WOMAN / FEMME ASSISE

92 HARLEQUIN / ARLEQUIN
Paris 1927 / Z VII: 80
oil on canvas, 31-3/4 x 25-1/2 in.,
80.6 x 64.7 cm.
signed 'Picasso/27' upper right
Related Works: Z VII: 73

Provenance: not given

Picasso Exhibitions: Paris 1932, no.
173; New York 1962, Tribute,
Rosenberg no. 47

lent by the Perls Galleries

Picasso's participation in the first
official Surrealist exhibition in 1925
does seem to have caused him to
explore different levels of personality
by symbols, which have the conviction
and also the irregularity of a dream.
Here, for example, the pale, ideal profile
on the left is confronted by the open-
mouthed, dark one on the right; but
whereas the classical one merges into
the wall the other extends into a
curious inverted 'L' with an eye at
either end. Framed by the dark profile
and the harlequin's bicorn hat is
another amorphous form with two dots
for eyes and a dark mouth surrounded
by a bracelet of white, rectangular
teeth. The effect is of a disturbing
evocation, rather than an analytical
investigation, of this harlequin who is
painted with highly controlled forms.

Although Picasso's paintings from 1925,
like this *Seated Woman*, possess something of the flat decorative quality one
can identify, legitimately, with synthetic
cubism and something of a fluid grace
one might associate, mistakenly, with
his classical style – neither quality can
explain the haunted effect of these
works. One of the difficulties is that the
distortions of the human body are so
much more organic than those of
cubism that, although they might not
be any more extreme, they are more
disturbing because of an illusion of
physiological probability. There is also
the occasional suggestion of trans-
formation into another natural form
like the breast at the right into a fish
and the fingers at the left into ripples of
water. At the same time these forms, no
matter how much they draw or pull
away, are brought together by the
never-ending movement of the contours and lines into shapes one would
assume to be like ectoplasm.

In the figures of this period some
suggestion of a more conventional
image of the human being exists like
the white back of the woman's head
– and there is almost always the
suggestion of the surprised recognition
by the conscious being (the right profile
here) of the submerged, dark and often
cockeyed unconscious world within
himself.

93 SEATED WOMAN / FEMME ASSISE

1926-1927 / Z VII: 81

oil on canvas, 51-1/2 x 38-1/2 in.,
130.7 x 97.7 cm.

signed 'Picasso / 27' centre right and
'1926-27' on the back

Provenance: Stephen C. Clark,
New York; anonymous gift to the
museum December 2, 1937

Picasso Exhibitions: Madrid 1936; New
York 1939, MMA no. 207; Mexico
1944; New York 1952, MMA;
New York 1956, Chalette no. 2; Oslo
1955, no. 71; Marseille 1959, no. 36;
New York 1962, MMA

lent by The Museum of Modern Art,
New York

94 PLATE II / PAINTER BETWEEN TWO
MODELS /
PEINTRE ENTRE DEUX MODELES

1927 / G 124

etching, 7-9/16 x 10-7/8 in.,
19.2 x 27.6 cm.

lent by The Museum of Modern Art,
New York. Gift of Henry Church

95 PLATE IV / PAINTER AND MODEL
KNITTING /
PEINTRE ET MODELE TRICOTANT

1927 / G 126

etching, 7-9/16 x 10-7/8 in.,
19.2 x 27.6 cm.

lent by The Museum of Modern Art,
New York. Gift of Henry Church

94

Although the special edition of the illustrations for Honoré de Balzac's *Le Chef d'Oeuvre Inconnu* (nos. 94 to 97) was issued by Ambroise Vollard in 1931 all but plate XIII (the *Table of Illustrations*) were etched by Picasso in 1927. These etchings have a classical beauty and clarity one associates with his earlier work from the 1920s and it is only at times one recognizes the free play of associations and the probing into different levels of meanings which suggests Picasso was not unaffected by Surrealism. He seems to have let his imagination wander freely in relation to the text. This cultivation of the strange associations of random ideas is apparent in plate X in which horses, the head of a bull, a male nude and female profiles and figures are brought together in a formal etching as if they were casual jottings on a sketchbook page.

These illustrations for *Le Chef d'Oeuvre Inconnu* are, however, primarily concerned with more conscious strata of meaning in the separate identities of the artist, the model and the work. The most famous and most obvious of these is plate IV, a more or less literal illustration of the Balzac novel in which the painter is working from a very real model, knitting, who appears upon his canvas as a linear pattern which seems more inspired by the wool than by the woman. In others this enigmatic confrontation of these three different worlds may not be as exaggerated but is equally fundamental.

95

96 PLATE X / NUDE SEATED
    SURROUNDED BY SKETCHES /
    NU ASSIS ENTOURE D'ESQUISSES

    1927 / G 132

    etching, 7-9/16 x 10-7/8 in.,
    19.2 x 27.6 cm.

    lent by Mr. Walter Carsen

97 PLATE XIII / TABLE OF
    ILLUSTRATIONS /
    TABLE DES EAUX-FORTES

    July 4, 1931 / G 135

    etching, 14-13/16 x 11-3/4 in.,
    37.5 x 29.8 cm.

    lent by Mr. M. F. Feheley

HEAD OF A YOUNG GIRL/FIGURE

DINARD

WOMAN IN RED ARMCHAIR/
FEMME AU FAUTEUIL ROUGE

98   HEAD OF A YOUNG GIRL/FIGURE
1928/Z VII: 122

oil on canvas, 20-7/8 x 12-1/2 in.,
53 x 31.7 cm.

signed 'Picasso' lower left

Related Works: Z VII: 119, 120, 121,
123-133; G 245

Provenance: Galka E. Scheyer;
bequest to the museum 1953

Picasso Exhibitions: San Antonio 1954,
no. 29; Houston 1955, no. 23; Los
Angeles 1961, UCLA no. 22

lent by The Pasadena Art Museum

98

In 1928 Picasso began to produce
strange heads which have an organic
character and unity which he often
emphasized, as he did it here, by
placing them against a geometric shape.
The division of the eyes, the shank of
hair and particularly the mouth which
is like a sewn incision seem eccentric
and even jauntily humorous rather
than disturbing.

99

In July 1928 at Dinard, Picasso had
made drawings which he had conceived as studies for a series of works
of sculpture or 'monuments' to be
placed on the promenade at Cannes.
Although the pen drawings for these,
which are usually larger than the paintings, are fairly awesome, the paintings
which emerged are small, lighthearted
and charming. This little canvas, for
example, seems full of blue sea, sun
and air. Only the bits of wood, from
which he apparently imagined the
figures formed, seem full of a strange
indigenous life which could be
disturbing.

101

The dehumanization which took place
in Picasso's treatment of the human
being in 1929 was greater than it had
been in his work since 1912 and 1913.
The forms in their wooden angularity
are just as far removed from any
organism as his papier collés, like the
1912 *Head* (no. 61), the 1913 *Harlequin*
(no. 63) or *Head of a Man* (no. 62), but
without any of the earlier impression
of playfulness. It may be the emphasis
upon the teeth, the pointing of the
breasts and the reduction of the hair to
three strands which makes the effect
of this head so alarming.

100   FIGURE
May 1929/G 246; M I: XXVI

lithograph, 9-3/8 x 5-9/16 in.,
23.7 x 14 cm.

signed 'Picasso mai XXIX' at the
bottom

Related Works: Z VII: 257

lent by The Museum of Modern Art,
New York
gift of Victor Riesenfeld

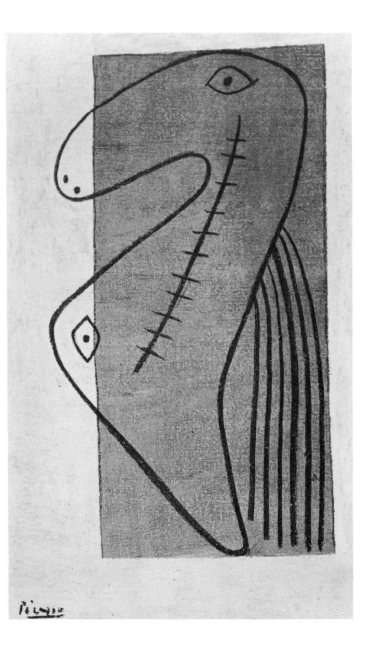

99 DINARD

Dinard 1928 / Z VII: 209

oil on canvas, 9-1/2 x 6-1/2 in.,
24.1 x 16.5 cm.

signed 'Picasso / 28' lower left

Related Works: Z VII: 190, 192, 194,
198-205, 208-216

Provenance: A. E. Gallatin; his gift
to the museum

lent by The Philadelphia Museum
of Art
A. E. Gallatin Collection

101 WOMAN IN RED ARMCHAIR/
FEMME AU FAUTEUIL ROUGE

1929 / Z VII: 294

oil on canvas, 25-1/2 x 21-1/4 in.,
64.7 x 53.9 cm.

signed 'Picasso/XXIX' upper right

Provenance: Alfred Flechtheim
Gallery, Berlin; James Johnson
Sweeney; Kootz Gallery, New York;
Mrs. Millicent Rogers; Alexander
Iolas Gallery, New York

Picasso Exhibitions: London 1962,
Arts Council no. 121

lent from a Private Collection

BUST OF A WOMAN / BUSTE DE FEMME

BUST OF A YOUNG GIRL /
BUSTE DE JEUNE FILLE

WOMAN IN AN ARMCHAIR /
FEMME DANS UN FAUTEUIL

102 BUST OF A WOMAN /
BUSTE DE FEMME

February 1929 / Z VII: 247

oil on canvas, 28-5/8 x 19-5/8 in.,
72.6 x 49.8 cm.

signed 'Picasso/29' upper left

Provenance: Wildenstein & Cie,
Paris; Valentine Galleries, New York;
Walter P. Chrysler, Jr., New York

Picasso Exhibitions: New York 1938,
Valentine no. 18

lent by Mr. and Mrs. Ralph F. Colin

This has often been titled *Sculpture
Nègre*, perhaps because the stiff,
wooden forms, the beaded teeth and
the concentrated force of the head
suggest African sculpture. Its savagery,
however, seems more Picasso's creation
in 1929. The frame on the wall sur-
rounds a dark area like an enigmatic,
unfathomable mirror, inevitably suggesting the magic one of the fairytale.
The mirror had begun to appear in
Picasso's work at this time as an
obvious symbol of other images of a
human being and reached its most
expressive use, of course, in the famous
Girl Before a Mirror (Z VII: 379) of
1932 in The Museum of Modern Art.

103

Picasso seems to have bisected this
young girl with the long hair and the
dress with a prim Peter Pan collar and
turned her head into·two forms which
confront each other with tongues like
knives. The left profile seems rigid and
afraid, the right placidly in repose.

104

In the lounging figure of this woman,
the warmth of the colour and the
suggestion of the sun on her body,
there are reminiscences of the summer
Picasso had spent at Dinard the year
before. She is freely painted with an
expressive force and spontaneity one
rarely finds in the works of this period.

103 BUST OF A YOUNG GIRL/
BUSTE DE JEUNE FILLE

March 1929 / Z VII: 245

oil on canvas, 28-3/4 x 23-5/8 in.,
73 x 60 cm.

signed 'Picasso/29' lower left

Provenance: not given

lent by the Perls Galleries

104 WOMAN IN AN ARMCHAIR/
FEMME DANS UN FAUTEUIL

March 2, 1929 / Z VII: 246

oil on canvas, 32 x 19-7/8 in.,
81.2 x 50.4 cm.

signed 'Picasso/XXIX' lower right

Related Works: Z VII: 249, 251

Provenance: not given

lent by the Perls Galleries

105 THE PAINTER AND HIS MODEL/
LE PEINTRE ET SON MODELE

1930 / G 247; M I: XXVII

lithograph, 9-3/8 x 11-7/16 in.,
23.2 x 28.9 cm.

lent by The National Gallery of
Canada, Ottawa

106 SEATED NUDE CROWNING HERSELF
WITH FLOWERS/
FEMME NUE SE COURONNANT DE
FLEURS

September 16, 1930 / G 195, Bolliger
no. 2, Arts Council 70

etching, 12-1/4 x 8-3/4 in.,
31 x 22.2 cm.

lent by The National Gallery of
Canada, Ottawa

107 SEATED NUDE

July 9, 1931 / G 208, Bolliger no. 8,
Arts Council 76

etching, 12-1/4 x 8-11/16 in.,
31 x 22 cm.

lent by The National Gallery of
Canada, Ottawa

107

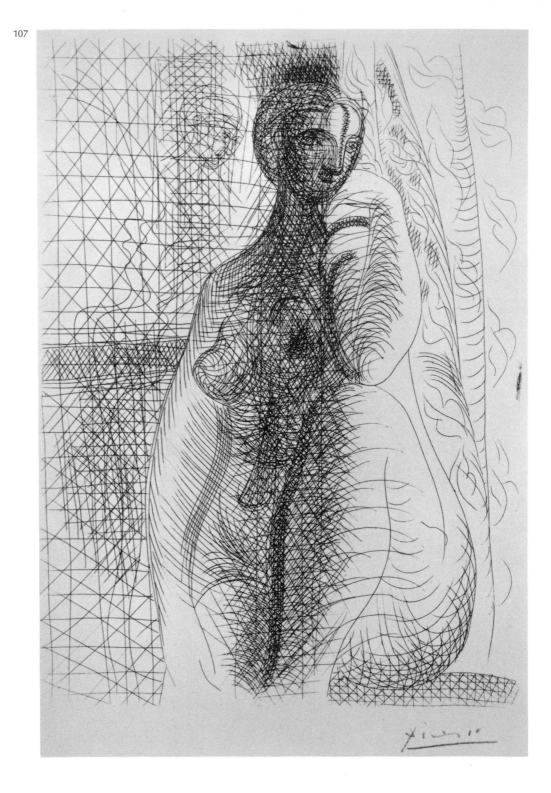

108 SEATED WOMAN/FEMME ASSISE

Boisgeloup, summer 1932/Z VII: 405

oil on panel, 29-1/4 x 20-5/8 in.,
74.2 x 52.3 cm.

not signed or dated

Provenance: Joseph Pulitzer, Jr.;
Valentine Dudensing, New York;
acquired by present owner 1938

Picasso Exhibitions: New York 1939,
MMA no. 249; New York 1962,
Tribute, Perls no. 6

lent by Mr. Lee A. Ault

In this monochromatic painting Picasso
painted his new mistress, Marie-Thérèse
Walter, conscious rather than asleep,
a thinker rather than a voluptuary.
Her profile recalls his classically
inspired paintings of the early twenties,
and also those profiles that would
insinuate themselves into his more
disturbed surrealist works like the
1927 *Harlequin* (no. 92). Any physiological curiosities like the eye which
appears twice or the finger nail which
becomes the lower lip, are made to
seem so inevitable that they do not
disturb the classical dignity and seriousness of this interpretation of Marie-
Thérèse.

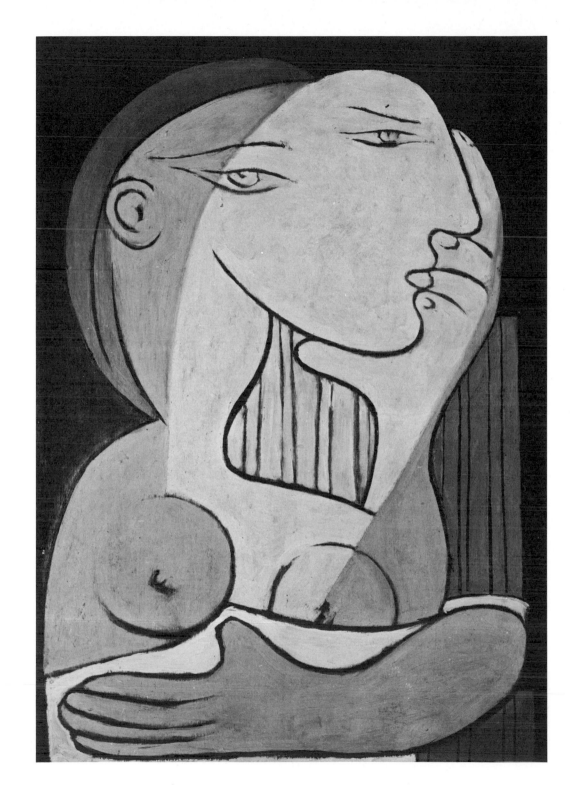

109 NUDE ON A BLACK COUCH/
NU AU FAUTEUIL NOIR

March 9, 1932 / Z VII: 377

oil on canvas, 63-1/2 x 50-1/4 in.,
161.2 x 127.6 cm.

signed 'Picasso/9 mars XXXII'
lower left

Related Works: Z VII: 331, 332,
382-388, 390, 396-403, 408-411

Provenance: acquired from the artist

Picasso Exhibitions: Paris 1932, no.
221; Paris 1936, Rosenberg no. 2; New
York 1939, MMA no. 244; New York
1945, Buchholz no. 10; New York 1948,
Rosenberg no. 19; Toronto 1949,
no. 21; São Paulo 1954, no. 26; New
York 1957, MMA p. 72; Philadelphia
1958, no. 127

lent by Mrs. Mary Callery
courtesy of The Baltimore Museum
of Art

These voluptuous nudes of 1932 were
inspired by the blond and, we are told,
placid Marie-Thérèse Walter. There are
drawings from 1931 which show
Picasso taking his bone-like meta-
morphic bodies (Z VII: 331) and
softening them (Z VII: 332) into
seductive flesh. Although in this
painting he still composed the body
somewhat freely, the swift movement
of the contours, the pale violet skin,
the golden hair, the petal-like hands
produce an effect of the most ideally
sensual sleep. The philodendron leaves
across the opened door may symbolize
its preoccupation.

110 RECLINING NUDE / NU COUCHE
Boisgeloup, July 1932 / Z VII: 407

oil on canvas, 40 x 36-1/2 in.,
101.5 x 92.6 cm.

signed 'Picasso' lower left

Studies: Z VII: 402

Related Works: Z VII: 311, 332,
382-388, 390, 396-401, 403, 408-411

Provenance: Kootz Gallery; acquired
by present owner 1956

Picasso Exhibitions: Milan 1953, no.
65; Rome 1953, no. 23; New York
1956, Kootz; New York 1962, Tribute,
Perls no. 4

lent by Mr. Peter A. Rübel

This smaller, later nude of those Picasso painted that year as if they were more erotic versions of Venetian sleeping Venuses, seems to express the fertility of the earth as much as the fertility of mankind. Lying on grass which is dappled with flowers like a mediaeval tapestry or Botticelli's *Prima Vera*, her hair is like a golden leaf and her legs have burst into flower. Her sleep is not as untroubled as no. 109 but even its restlessness seems to be part of its force.

111 BATHER WITH A BALL/
BAIGNEUSE AU BORD DE LA MER

Boisgeloup, August 30, 1932 / Z VIII: 147 (1933)

oil on canvas, 57-1/2 x 45 in., 146 x 114.2 cm.

signed 'Picasso' lower left and dated on the back

Provenance: Kootz Gallery, New York; acquired by present owner April 1960

Picasso Exhibtions: Milan 1953, no. 63; New York 1957, MMA p. 69; Philadelphia 1958, no. 129; London 1960, Arts Council no. 131; New York 1962, Tribute, Perls no. 3

lent from the Collection of Victor W. Ganz

The most ebullient tribute of Picasso's affection for Marie-Thérèse may have been this buoyant figure in the lavender bathing costume. It is as if he had remembered his miniature paintings of bathers at Dinard the summer of 1928 and decided to do somewhat the same thing on a large scale, swell the bather and soften her, wash the setting with a gentle light, remove the ominous key from the bathhouse door and make the ball as beautiful and as eternally remote as the moon. Even if this endearing bather does express some alarm (in her rear profile) and an uncanny concentration, her chief function seems to be to amuse us and to make the world, therefore, a happier place.

112 PLASTER BUST AND COMPOTE/
NATURE MORTE

Paris, January 29, 1933 / Z VIII: 84

oil on canvas, 28-7/8 x 36-1/4 in.,
73.3 x 92 cm.

signed 'Picasso/XXXIII' upper right
'Paris Dimanche 29 janvier XXXIII'
on the back

Studies: drawing in the E. Beyeler
Collection, Basel

Provenance: Pierre Matisse Gallery;
acquired by present owners October
7, 1937

Picasso Exhibitions: Boston 1938; New
York 1939, MMA no. 256; São Paulo
1954, no. 29; Paris 1955, Décoratifs
no. 81

lent from the Collection of Mr. and
Mrs. Joseph Pulitzer, Jr.

With the purchase of the château at
Boisgeloup in 1930 Picasso began to
spend more time on sculpture, occasionally with his old friend, the Spanish
welder, Gonzalez. Barr (p. 178) points
out that he seems to have turned to it
with particular concentration after the
great retrospective exhibition of his
work in Paris in June 1932. Although
most of the heads he made out of
plaster are more restful than the one he
painted in this still life of January 1933,
they seem equally giantesque and
freely formed. In this one painting there
is an overt contradiction between the
strongly plastic piece of sculpture and
the light piece of still life painting on
the right, as if it were another expression of Picasso's consciousness of his
work or his 'art' at this time.

During the spring of 1933 and again during the late winter and spring of 1934 Picasso worked on a series of etchings which, like his etchings for Balzac's *Le Chef d'Oeuvre Inconnu*, were concerned with the relationships between the artist, his model and his work: this was *The Sculptor's Studio*, nos. 113 to 133. It is interesting that the artist is now represented as a sculptor, which Picasso had become with the purchase of the château at Boisgeloup, and is normally a bearded man, perhaps a reference to the fact that Picasso was now over fifty. Although not specifically autobiographical and without any apparent narrative development these etchings seem like a group of revealing lyric poems.

The Sculptor's Studio can make us realize that in some ways the classical generalizations of the early 1920s had never ceased, that even the grotesque and immediate effects of the paintings of the late twenties were no more specific about an environment. Certainly here the beautiful nude bodies in themselves imply a world far removed from twentieth century society – and a world quite specifically associated with the classical past. It is spacious, sunlit, unhurried.

The sensuality which Picasso had expressed in his work from the beginning of his love affair with Marie-Thérèse, is revealed overtly here in many prints of the sculptor lying quietly with a woman by his side. It is also suggested in the firmly rounded forms of the bodies. There is a similar sensuality in the response to the works of art – a gentle touch, a caress, the

complete absorption of a face.

This state of ideal quiet in these prints, which seems to encourage a gentle sensuality which can be satisfied, also seems to permit the imagination to perform freely without destroying the classical serenity. It appears, for example, in the ease with which he places a row of anemones through the head of a seated nude woman. Before the sculptor and his companion there often appear the visions of ballerinas, horses and bulls, and rapes, which in their energy and complication could have been imagined by some Hellenistic sculptor.

The consistently classical style of *The Sculptor's Studio* is only rarely disturbed by a construction which, in its modernity and in its tenseness, pulls us back to the twentieth century and to another aspect of Picasso. On the whole it represents that ideal harmony of the sensual, the imaginative and the passive which Picasso seems to have experienced with Marie-Thérèse.

Most of these etchings are from The National Gallery of Canada which in 1957 acquired a set of all 100 prints from the *Vollard Suite*.

113 SEATED MODEL AND SCULPTOR STUDYING SCULPTURED HEAD
c. March 1933/Vollard Suite, Bolliger no. 38, Arts Council no. 117
etching, 10-1/2 x 7-5/8 in., 26.7 x 19.4 cm.
lent by Mr. Walter Carsen

114 SCULPTOR AND MODEL VIEWING STATUE OF SEATED WOMAN
c. 1933/Vollard Suite, Bolliger no. 40, Arts Council no. 118
dry point, 12-7/16 x 7-1/4 in., 31.6 x 18.4 cm.

115 SEATED NUDE WITH PAINTING AND SCULPTURED HEAD
Paris, March 21, 1933/ Vollard Suite, Bolliger no. 43, Arts Council no. 82
etching, 10-9/16 x 7-5/8 in., 26.8 x 19.4 cm.

116 SCULPTOR WITH FISHBOWL, NUDE AND SCULPTURED HEAD
Paris, March 21?, 1933/Vollard Suite, Bolliger no. 44, Arts Council no. 83
etching, 10-1/2 x 7-5/8 in., 26.7 x 19.4 cm.

117 YOUNG SCULPTOR AT WORK
Paris, March 25, 1933/Vollard Suite, Bolliger no. 46, Arts Council no. 86
etching, 10-1/2 x 7-5/8 in., 26.7 x 19.4 cm.

118 SEATED SCULPTOR AND TWO SCULPTURED HEADS
Paris, March 26, 1933/Vollard Suite, Bolliger no. 48, Arts Council no. 89
etching, 10-1/2 x 7-5/8 in., 26.7 x 19.4 cm.

119 SCULPTOR, MODEL AND STATUE OF A NUDE
Paris, March 27, 1933/Vollard Suite, Bolliger no. 51, Arts Council no. 90
etching, 10-1/2 x 7-5/8 in., 26.7 x 19.4 cm.

120 SCULPTOR, RECLINING MODEL, AND SCULPTURE OF A HORSE AND YOUTH
Paris, March 30, 1933/Vollard Suite, Bolliger no. 55, Arts Council no. 94
etching, 7-5/8 x 10-9/16 in., 19.4 x 26.8 cm.

121 SCULPTOR SEATED BY A WINDOW WORKING FROM MODEL
Paris, March 31, 1933/Vollard Suite, Bolliger no. 59, Arts Council no. 99
etching, 7-5/8 x 10-1/2 in., 19.4 x 26.7 cm.

122 SCULPTOR AT REST, RECLINING MODEL AND SCULPTURE
Paris, March 31?, 1933/Vollard Suite, Bolliger no. 60, Arts Council no. 98
etching, 7-5/8 x 10-1/2 in., 19.4 x 26.7 cm.

123 MODEL AND SCULPTURED HEAD
Paris, April 1, 1933/Vollard Suite, Bolliger no. 61, Arts Council no. 100
etching, 10-1/2 x 7-5/8 in., 26.7 x 19.4 cm.

124 SCULPTOR AND RECLINING MODEL VIEWING SCULPTURED HEAD
Paris, April 2, 1933/Vollard Suite, Bolliger no. 62, Arts Council no. 101
etching, 7-5/8 x 10-1/2 in., 19.4 x 26.7 cm.

125 MODEL KNEELING BY A WINDOW VIEWING A SCULPTURE OF NUDE FIGURES AND A REARING HORSE
Paris, April 5, 1933/Vollard Suite, Bolliger no. 66, Arts Council no. 105
etching, 11-11/16 x 14-7/16 in., 29.6 x 36.6 cm.

126 HEADS OF SCULPTOR AND MODEL AND STATUE OF A STRIDING YOUTH
Paris, April 11, 1933/Vollard Suite, Bolliger no. 70, Arts Council no. 109
etching, 10-1/2 x 7-5/8 in., 26.7 x 19.4 cm.
Nos. 114 to 126 lent by The National Gallery of Canada, Ottawa

127 FEMALE MODEL AND TWO SCULPTURES
Paris, May 3, 1933/Vollard Suite, Bolliger no. 72, Arts Council no. 111
etching, 14-15/16 x 11-11/16 in., 38 x 29.6 cm.
lent by Mr. Walter Carsen

128 MODEL AND SCULPTURED FEMALE TORSO
Paris, May 4, 1933/Vollard Suite, Bolliger no. 73, Arts Council no. 112
combined technique, 10-9/16 x 7-9/16 in., 26.8 x 19.2 cm.

129 MODEL AND SURREALIST
    SCULPTURE
    Paris, May 4, 1933/Vollard Suite,
    Bolliger no. 74, Arts Council no. 113
    etching, 10-9/16 x 7-5/8 in.,
    26.8 x 19.4 cm.

130 CROUCHING MODEL, NUDE, AND
    SCULPTURED HEAD
    Paris, May 5, 1933/Vollard Suite,
    Bolliger no. 75, Arts Council no. 114
    combined technique, 10-1/2 x
    7-5/8 in., 26.7 x 19.4 cm.

131 SCULPTURE OF SEATED NUDE,
    SCULPTURED HEAD AND VASE
    OF FLOWERS
    Paris, May 5, 1933/Vollard Suite,
    Bolliger no. 76, Arts Council no. 115
    combined technique, 10-1/2 x
    7-9/16 in., 26.7 x 19.2 cm.

132 TWO NUDES
    Paris, January 27, 1934/Vollard Suite,
    Bolliger no. 78, Arts Council no. 121
    etching, 10-15/16 x 7-13/16 in.,
    27.8 x 19.8 cm.

133 FOUR MODELS AND A
    SCULPTURED HEAD
    Paris, March 10, 1934/Vollard Suite,
    Bolliger no. 82, Arts Council no. 125
    combined technique, 8-9/16 x
    12-1/4 in., 21.7 x 31 cm.

134 TWO NUDES BATHING
    Paris, May 22, 1933/Vollard Suite,
    Bolliger no. 14, Arts Council no. 142
    combined technique, 7-5/8 x
    10-9/16 in., 19.4 x 26.8 cm.

135 BATTLE OF LOVE: THE EMBRACE
    c. 1933/Vollard Suite, Bolliger no. 29
    Arts Council no. 129
    combined technique, 7-13/16 x
    10-7/8 in., 19.8 x 27.6 cm.

136 HEAD OF REMBRANDT AND STUDIES
    January 27, 1934/Vollard Suite,
    Bolliger no. 34, Arts Council no. 147
    10-15/16 x 7-13/16 in., 27.7 x 19.8 cm.

    Nos. 128 to 136 lent by The National
    Gallery of Canada, Ottawa

137 PORTRAIT OF REMBRANDT AND
    STANDING NUDE
    January 31, 1934/Vollard Suite,
    Bolliger no. 36, Arts Council no. 148
    etching, 10-15/16 x 7-13/16 in.,
    27.7 x 19.8 cm.
    lent by Professor and Mrs.
    Gilbert Bagnani

138 SEATED NUDE
    Paris, March 9, 1934/Vollard Suite,
    Bolliger no. 21, Arts Council no. 153
    dry point, 10-15/16 x 7-13/16 in.,
    27.7 x 19.8 cm.
    lent by The National Gallery of
    Canada, Ottawa

139 BULL, HORSE AND WOMAN
    Paris, June 20, 1934/Vollard Suite,
    Bolliger no. 22, Arts Council no. 156
    combined technique, 11-11/16 x
    9-5/16 in., 29.8 x 23.6 cm.
    lent by The National Gallery of
    Canada, Ottawa

140 LYSISTRATA: COUNCIL OF WOMEN
    1934
    8-11/16 x 5-15/16 in., 22 x 15 cm.

141 LYSISTRATA: KINESIAS AND
    MYRRHINE
    1934
    etching, 8-11/16 x 5-3/4 in.,
    22 x 14.5 cm.

142 LYSISTRATA: KINESIAS AND
    MYRRHINE WITH A CHILD
    1934
    etching, 8-5/16 x 5-7/16 in.,
    21 x 13.7 cm.

143 LYSISTRATA: TWO DEJECTED MEN
    ON SEASHORE
    February 5, 1934
    etching, 8-5/16 x 5-7/16 in.,
    21 x 13.7 cm.

144 LYSISTRATA: NEGOTIATIONS
    BETWEEN ATHENIANS AND
    SPARTAN ENVOYS
    1934
    etching, 8-11/16 x 5-15/16 in.,
    22 x 15 cm.

145 LYSISTRATA: CELEBRATION
    OF PEACE
    1934
    etching, 8-11/16 x 5-15/16 in.,
    22 x 15 cm.

    Nos. 140 to 145 The Art Gallery of
    Toronto

146 CANNES

July 17, 1933 / not in Z

watercolour, 15-3/4 x 19-1/2 in.,
40 x 49.5 cm.

signed 'Picasso/Cannes 17 juillet
XXXIII' lower right

Provenance: acquired by present
owners about 1953

lent by Mr. and Mrs. John David Eaton

In this delicate and romantic watercolour the profile of Marie-Thérèse
upon the ruined wall seems as beautiful
and as eternal as a piece of classical
sculpture whereas, before her, stands a
figure so ephemeral that the wind is
threatening his fragile existence. One is
tempted to see in it an allegory in
which Picasso recognizes the frailty
even of his love for Marie-Thérèse.

147 TWO FIGURES ON THE BEACH/
DEUX FIGURES

Cannes, July 28, 1933 / Z VIII: 124

pen and ink, 15-3/4 x 20 in.,
40 x 50.7 cm.

signed 'Picasso/Cannes 28 juillet
XXXIII' lower right

Provenance: acquired by the museum
1939

Picasso Exhibitions: New York 1939,
MMA no. 258; Toronto 1949, no. 51;
New York 1962, MMA

lent by The Museum of Modern Art,
New York
Purchase Fund

One cannot help feel that this drawing acknowledges the official Surrealists of the 1930s and in particular, of course, Picasso's fellow countryman Salvador Dalí whom he had met in 1928. The combination of disembodied limbs and furniture, the flying fork and the suspended glove suggest the other painter. It is drawn in the curiously nervous style Picasso employed for other drawings of this kind and time. According to Jardot (no. 87) this is one of the few drawings from this period that Picasso admits as being Surrealist in character.

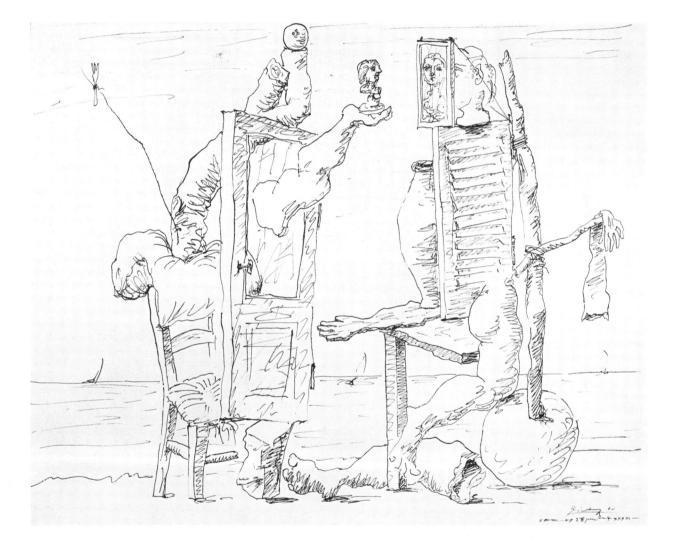

148 BATHERS ON THE BEACH/
FEMMES SUR LA PLAGE

Paris, April 24, 1934/not in Z

watercolour, 9-3/4 x 13-1/2 in.,
24.8 x 34.2 cm.

signed 'Picasso/PARIS/24 Avril
XXXIV' lower left

Related Works: Z VIII: 187

Provenance: Michel Warren, Paris;
acquired by the gallery 1962

lent by the Jerrold Morris
International Gallery

This watercolour is related to one
(Z VIII: 187) dated two days later in
which the head appearing out of the
water becomes a beautiful, omniscient
woman hovering over the sea. Another
female figure has the rectangular head
of the central figure here; it is a form
also found in some of the plaster pieces
of sculpture Picasso was doing at
Boisgeloup that year.

149 TWO GIRLS READING/
DEUX PERSONNAGES

Boisgeloup, March 28, 1934/Z VIII: 193

oil on canvas, 32 x 25-1/2 in.,
81.2 x 64.7 cm.

not signed or dated

Related Works: Z VIII: 183, 190, 191,
192, 194

Provenance: Valentine Galleries, New
York; purchased by Mrs. John W.
Garrett November 16, 1937,
bequeathed by Mrs. Garrett to the
Evergreen House Foundation 1952

Picasso Exhibtions: New York 1936,
Valentine; New York 1939, MMA
no. 265

lent by the Evergreen House
Foundation

This is the freest and richest of a series
of paintings Picasso made at Boisgeloup
of a fair and a dark-haired girl reading
together. The blond is quite naturally
suggestive of Marie-Thérèse – in her
relative passivity, her self-absorption
and even a certain possible narcis-
sicism, the two parts of her face like a
continuous caress. The darker girl in
her nervousness seems more responsive to externals, almost as if she were
an anticipation of the mistress who was
to succeed Marie-Thérèse, Dora Maar.

At Boisgeloup in April 1933 Picasso
began to make drawings (Z VIII: 100,
101) of a creature, which was only
partly human, violating a woman who
often resembled Marie-Thérèse. By May
he had appeared in Picasso's prints
(nos. 150 to 152) as the minotaur. This
being, which was half-human and half-
bull, had of course the most ancient of
classical associations with the Mediterranean island of Crete and was, therefore, a natural figure to suggest the
antiquity of animal sensuousness and
lust. Picasso made him a happy, con-
vivial companion, occasionally with a
glass of champagne in his hand, and
finally showed real compassion for him
as he lay dying in an arena. In one print
a row of women look down at the
dying figure unhappily and one of them
puts out her hand compassionately
toward him.

A year later in October, Picasso did a
series of four etchings of the *Blinded
Minotaur* in which he seems, like
Oedipus, a strange prophetic figure as
he walks easily with his powerful body
but must be guided by a gentle little
girl with a dove, who resembles Marie-
Thérèse. Finally in 1935 Picasso did a
major etching, the *Minotauromachy*,
in which the blinded minotaur is now
ominous as he hovers over a small
horse with the dead body of a semi-
nude woman in a matador's costume
upon its back.

150 DRINKING MINOTAUR AND
SCULPTOR WITH TWO MODELS
Paris, May 18, 1933 / Vollard Suite
no. 85
combined technique, 11-11/16 x
14-3/8 in., 29.8 x 36.5 cm.

151 DYING MINOTAUR
Paris, May 26, 1933 / Vollard Suite
no. 88
combined technique, 7-5/8 x
10-1/2 in., 19.4 x 26.7 cm.

152 DYING MINOTAUR IN ARENA
Paris, May 30, 1933 / Vollard Suite
no. 90
etching, 7-3/4 x 10-9/16 in.,
19.6 x 26.8 cm.

153 MINOTAUR, DRINKING SCULPTOR
AND THREE MODELS
Boisgeloup, June 18, 1933 / Vollard
Suite no. 92
combined technique, 11-11/16 x
14-3/8 in., 29.8 x 36.5 cm.
Nos. 150 to 153 lent by The National
Gallery of Canada, Ottawa

155 THE BLIND MINOTAUR
Paris, October 23, 1934 / Vollard
Suite no. 96
etching, 9-3/8 x 11-3/4 in.,
23.8 x 29.8 cm.

156 THE BLIND MINOTAUR
October 1934 / Vollard Suite no. 95
etching and engraving,
8-15/16 x 12-5/16 in., 22.7 x 31.1 cm.

157 THE BLIND MINOTAUR
October 1934 / Vollard Suite no. 97
etching and aquatint,
9-11/16 x 13-5/8 in., 24.5 x 34.5 cm.
Nos. 154 to 157 lent by The Museum
of Modern Art, New York
No. 157 Mrs. John D. Rockefeller, Jr.,
Purchase Fund

158 MINOTUROMACHY
1935
etching, 19-1/2 x 27-3/8 in.,
49.5 x 69.4 cm.
lent by The Brooklyn Museum

154 THE BLIND MINOTAUR
Boisgeloup, September 22, 1934 /
Vollard Suite no. 94
etching and engraving,
9-15/16 x 13-5/8 in., 25.3 x 34.5 cm.

159 TWO MEN WITH MINOTAUR AND
SCULPTURED BULL
c. 1935 / Vollard Suite no. 24
combined technique, 9-3/4 x
13-5/8 in., 24.8 x 34.5 cm.
lent by The National Gallery of
Canada, Ottawa

160 SEATED NUDE AND THREE STUDIES
OF A HEAD
c. 1935 / Vollard Suite no. 25
combined technique, 5-1/8 x 7 in.,
13 x 17.8 cm.
lent by The National Gallery of
Canada, Ottawa

161 VIGIL
1936
etching and aquatint, 9-1/4 x 11-5/8 in.,
23.5 x 29.5 cm.
lent by The Museum of Modern Art,
New York. Purchase Fund

162 SATYR AND SLEEPING WOMAN
June 12, 1936
etching and aquatint, 12-7/16 x
16-7/16 in., 31.5 x 41.7 cm.
lent by The Museum of Modern Art,
New York. Purchase Fund

163 AMBROISE VOLLARD
1936
aquatint, 9-11/16 x 13-3/4 in.,
24.5 x 34.9 cm.
lent by The Museum of Modern Art,
New York
acquired through the Lillie P. Bliss
Bequest

164 THE POET'S ATTIC/
INTERIEUR A LA FEMME ENDORMIE

December 18, 1936 / Z VIII: 309

oil on canvas, 38-1/4 x 51-1/4 in.,
97 x 130 cm.

signed '18 D. XXXVI. Picasso' lower
left

Related Works: Z VIII: 249, 251,
253-256, 261-266

Provenance: Carlo Frua de Angeli
Collection, Milan

Picasso Exhibitions: São Paulo 1954,
no. 32

lent by the Perls Galleries

Although the idea of the woman sleeping with her head on the table suggests a series Picasso had painted of two women almost two years before, this work has a strange sobriety compared with those works (for example, Z VIII: 256 in the Musée d'Art Moderne in Paris).

The grisaille palette and the austere setting give it a monkishness suggestive of a twentieth century Zurbaran, an effect which the female form does, however, somewhat disturb. It is interesting in its anticipation of certain effects – the colour and the light bulb, for example – which Picasso would use a few months later for his great work, the *Guernica*.

Although Picasso seems to have been only indirectly affected by the First World War, as a Spaniard he became passionately committed to the loyalist side of the Civil War in Spain. He contributed money to the Republican Government and even became the honourary director of the Prado Museum, a post he regarded with a certain seriousness. Late in 1937 Picasso sent a statement which was read at a meeting of the American Artists' Congress in New York and in which he said in part (Barr p. 264), 'It is my wish at this time to remind you that I have always believed and still believe, that artists who live and work with spiritual values cannot and should not remain indifferent to a conflict in which the highest values of humanity and civilization are at stake.'

On January 8 and 9, 1937, Picasso etched the first states of fourteen prints which were to make up *The Dream and Lie of Franco,* for which he also wrote a poem. With a quick etched line he called upon his experience producing surrealist imagery to create an obscene symbol for General Franco, and he used the horse as an object of human pity and sympathy as he had in the *Minotauromachy* (no. 158), and the bull as a symbol of beneficent power against Franco (in one etching his head forming the shape of the map of Spain). Human beauty, which Franco attacks rather helplessly with a frail sledgehammer, or which lies dead upon a battle field, is represented by a woman of the classical beauty of Marie-Thérèse.

On April 28th word reached Paris that German bombers fighting for Franco had on April 26th completely wiped out the small Spanish town of Guernica, and three days later Picasso began to make studies on the theme of this destruction for a painting he had already promised for the Spanish Pavilion of the Paris World's Fair that year. As he said in May (Barr p. 202) 'In the panel on which I am working which I shall call *Guernica,* and in all my recent works of art, I clearly express my abhorrence of the military caste which has sunk Spain in an ocean of pain and death.'

Although the finished painting cannot be moved from The Museum of Modern Art in New York, where it is housed, the sketches for the work are exhibited here through the courtesy of the artist and The Museum of Modern Art.

On May 1st, the first day he worked toward the *Guernica,* Picasso in four rapid sketches on blue paper and one gesso panel produced a flegmatic bull, a tortured, dying horse, and a woman who appears through a window at the right and holds forth a light with an arm which has the power of the mother's arm in Raphael's *Figure in the Borgo* or even of the arm of New York's *Statue of Liberty.* There is also a small Pegasus (a symbol of hope?) who flies out of the stomach of the dying horse in the gesso panel but disappears in the later studies.

The next day Picasso studied the head of the horse, making use of the pointed tongue, which in earlier paintings (no. 103) he had used with a certain wit, as an expression instead of painful will to survive. On May 8th he began to work on an image of a mother crawling with a dead child held between her naked breasts. The next day he made an even more tortured study of the mother carrying the dead child up a ladder, while her own head falls back in anguish and despair. And he also worked upon the composition again. On May 10th he began to make studies, strongly contrasted in mood, of the quiet, human-faced bull and a grotesque, tortured horse.

Although even in the gesso study of May 1st Picasso had arrived at the form for the head of the woman and had made it firmer in his later studies of the mother with a dead child, it was apparently May 13th before he began to study it independently, refining the tortured shapes of the lips, the teeth, the tongue and the eyes. And it was May 20th and May 24th before he began to give her a sword-like tongue and play with the surface of her face so that her very being seems like a shriek of pain. These studies, which he continued even after he had finished painting the *Guernica,* had their own independent meaning for Picasso. He also used them, along with other figures he had developed for the painting, in the four scenes he added to *The Dream and Lie of Franco* in its

third state which he etched on June 7th.

Although one can think of a *Fire in the Borgo* and *Massacres of the Innocents* and *Sabine Women* by artists like Raphael, Guido Reni, Poussin and David as having anticipated parts of what Picasso had done in the *Guernica,* its large monochromatic surface, which Picasso finished to be placed in the Spanish Pavilion early in June, seems to have expressed, with more passionate conviction than any other artist except perhaps his fellow countryman Goya has done, the absolute horror and futility of war.

165 THE DREAM AND LIE OF FRANCO
January 8 – June 7, 1937
etching and aquatint,
12-3/8 x 15-5/8 in., 31.4 x 39.6 cm.

166 COMPOSITIONAL STUDY I
May 1, 1937 / Z IX: 1
pencil on blue paper,
8-1/4 x 10-5/8 in., 20.9 x 26.9 cm.
dated upper left

167 COMPOSITIONAL STUDY II
May 1, 1937 / Z IX: 2
pencil on blue paper,
8-1/4 x 10-5/8 in., 20.9 x 26.9 cm.
dated upper left

168 COMPOSITIONAL STUDY III
May 1, 1937 / Z IX: 3
pencil on blue paper,
8-1/4 x 10-5/8 in., 20.9 x 26.9 cm.
dated upper left

169 STUDY IV – A HORSE
May 1, 1937 / Z IX: 4
pencil on blue paper,
8-1/4 x 10-5/8 in., 20.9 x 26.9 cm.
dated upper right

170 STUDY V – A HORSE
May 1, 1937 / Z IX: 5
pencil on blue paper,
8-1/4 x 10-5/8 in., 20.9 x 26.9 cm.
dated upper right

171 COMPOSITIONAL STUDY
May 1, 1937 / Z IX: 10
pencil on gesso on wood,
21-1/8 x 25-1/2 in., 53.6 x 64.7 cm.
not dated

172 HORSE'S HEAD I
May 2, 1937 / Z IX: 6
pencil on blue paper,
8-1/4 x 6 in., 20.9 x 15.2 cm.
dated upper left

173 HORSE'S HEAD II
May 2, 1937 / Z IX: 7
pencil on blue paper,
10-1/2 x 8-1/4 in., 26.6 x 20.9 cm.
dated upper left

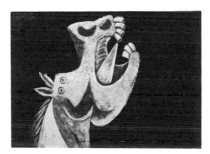

174 HORSE'S HEAD
May 2, 1937 / Z IX: 11
oil on canvas, 25-1/2 x 36-1/4 in.,
64.7 x 92 cm.
dated upper left

175 HORSE AND BULL
early May ? / Z IX: 9
pencil on tan paper,
8-7/8 x 4-3/4 in., 22.5 x 12 cm.
not dated

176 COMPOSITIONAL STUDY
May 8, 1937 / Z IX: 13
pencil, 9-1/2 x 17-7/8 in.,
24.1 x 45.3 cm.
dated lower left

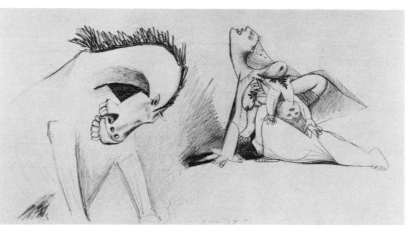

177 HORSE, AND MOTHER WITH
DEAD CHILD
May 8, 1937 / Z IX: 12
pencil, 9-1/2 x 17-7/8 in.,
24.1 x 45.3 cm.
dated bottom centre

178 MOTHER WITH DEAD CHILD
May 9, 1937 / Z IX: 14
ink, 9-1/2 x 17-7/8 in., 24.1 x 45.3 cm.
dated lower left

179 COMPOSITION STUDY
May 9, 1937 / Z IX: 18
pencil, 9-1/2 x 17-7/8 in.,
24.1 x 45.3 cm.
dated centre right

180 MOTHER WITH DEAD CHILD
ON LADDER
May 9, 1937 / Z IX: 16
pencil, 17-7/8 x 9-1/2 in.,
45.3 x 24.1 cm.
dated lower left

181 STUDY FOR THE HORSE – I
May 10, 1937 / Z IX: 17
pencil, 9-1/2 x 17-7/8 in.,
24.1 x 45.3 cm.
dated lower right

182 STUDY FOR THE HORSE – II
May 10, 1937 / Z IX: 21
pencil, 17-7/8 x 9-1/2 in.,
45.3 x 24.1 cm.
dated upper centre

183 BULL'S HEAD WITH
HUMAN FACE – III
May 10, 1937 / Z IX: 20
pencil, 17-7/8 x 9-1/2 in.,
45.3 x 24.1 cm.
dated lower left

184 STUDY FOR THE HORSE – IV
May 10, 1937 / Z IX: 19
pencil and coloured crayon,
9-1/2 x 17-7/8 in., 24.1 x 45.3 cm.
dated upper right

185 MOTHER WITH DEAD CHILD
ON LADDER – V
May 10, 1937 / Z IX: 15
coloured crayon and pencil,
17-7/8 x 9-1/2 in., 45.3 x 24.1 cm.
dated lower left

186 BULL WITH HUMAN FACE
May 11, 1937 / Z IX: 23
pencil, 9-1/2 x 17-7/8 in.,
24.1 x 45.3 cm.
dated lower left

187 WOMAN'S HEAD – I
May 13, 1937 / Z IX: 22
pencil and coloured crayon,
17-7/8 x 9-1/2 in., 45.3 x 24.1 cm.
dated lower right

188 HAND WITH BROKEN SWORD – II
May 13, 1937 / Z IX: 24
pencil, 9-1/2 x 17-7/8 in.,
24.1 x 45.3 cm.
dated lower right

189 MOTHER WITH DEAD CHILD – III
May 13, 1937 / Z IX: 25
coloured crayon and pencil,
9-1/2 x 17-7/8 in., 24.1 x 45.3 cm.
dated upper right

190 HORSE'S HEAD
May 20, 1937 / Z IX: 27
pencil and wash, 11-1/2 x 9-1/4 in.,
29.1 x 23.4 cm.
dated upper left

191 HORSE'S HEAD
May 20, 1937 / Z IX: 26
pencil and wash, 9-1/4 x 11-1/2 in.,
23.4 x 29.1 cm.
dated upper centre

192 BULL'S HEAD
May 20, 1937 / Z IX: 28
pencil and wash, 9-1/4 x 11-1/2 in.,
23.4 x 29.1 cm.
dated right centre

193 BULL'S HEAD
May 20, 1937 / Z IX: 29
pencil and wash, 9-1/4 x 11-1/2 in.,
23.4 x 29.1 cm.

194 WOMAN'S HEAD
May 20, 1937 / Z IX: 32
pencil and wash, 11-1/2 x 9-1/4 in.,
29.1 x 23.4 cm.
dated upper right

195 WEEPING HEAD
May 24, 1937 / Z IX: 31
pencil and wash, 11-1/2 x 9-1/4 in.,
29.1 x 23.4 cm.
dated upper left

196 WEEPING HEAD
May 24, 1937 / Z IX: 33
pencil and wash, 11-1/2 x 9-1/4 in.,
29.1 x 23.4 cm.
dated upper left

197 HEAD
May 24, 1937 / Z IX: 30
pencil and gouache, 9-1/4 x 11-1/2 in.,
23.4 x 29.1 cm.
dated upper right

198 WEEPING HEAD
May 27, 1937 / Z IX: 36
pencil and wash, 9-1/4 x 11-1/2 in.,
23.4 x 29.1 cm.
dated upper left

199 FALLING MAN
May 27, 1937 / Z IX: 34
pencil and wash, 9-1/4 x 11-1/2 in.,
23.4 x 29.1 cm.
dated lower left

200 MOTHER WITH DEAD CHILD
May 28, 1937 / Z IX: 37
pencil, coloured crayon, gouache and
hair, 9-1/4 x 11-1/2 in., 23.4 x 29.1 cm.
dated lower left

201 MOTHER WITH DEAD CHILD
May 28, 1937 / Z IX: 38
pencil, coloured crayon and gouache,
9-1/4 x 11-1/2 in., 23.4 x 29.1 cm.
dated upper left

202 WEEPING HEAD
May 28, 1937 / Z IX: 35
pencil, coloured crayon and gouache,
9-1/4 x 11-1/2 in., 23.4 x 29.1 cm.
dated upper right

203 WEEPING HEAD
May 31, 1937 / Z IX: 39
pencil, coloured crayon and gouache,
9-1/4 x 11-1/2 in., 23.4 x 29.1 cm.
dated upper left

204 WEEPING HEAD
June 3, 1937 / Z IX: 40
pencil, coloured crayon and gouache,
9-1/4 x 11-1/2 in., 23.4 x 29.1 cm.
dated upper left

205 WEEPING HEAD
June 3, 1937 / Z IX: 41
pencil, coloured crayon and gouache,
9-1/4 x 11-1/2 in., 23.4 x 29.1 cm.
dated upper centre

206 WEEPING HEAD
June 3, 1937 / Z IX: 44
pencil, coloured crayon and gouache,
9-1/4 x 11-1/2 in., 23.4 x 29.1 cm.
dated lower right

207 HEAD AND HORSE'S HOOFS
June 3, 1937 / Z IX: 45
pencil and wash, 9-1/4 x 11-1/2 in.,
23.4 x 29.1 cm.
dated upper left

208 STUDY FOR MAN'S HEAD
June 4, 1937 / Z IX: 42
pencil and wash, 9-1/4 x 11-1/2 in.,
23.4 x 29.1 cm.
dated centre right

209 STUDY OF A HAND
June 4, 1937 / Z IX: 43
pencil and wash, 9-1/4 x 11-1/2 in.,
23.4 x 29.1 cm.
dated bottom centre

210 WEEPING HEAD
June 8, 1937 / Z IX: 46
pencil, coloured crayon and wash,
11-1/2 x 9-1/4 in., 29.1 x 23.4 cm.
dated upper left

211 WEEPING HEAD
June 8, 1937 / Z IX: 48
pencil and wash, 11-1/2 x 9-1/4 in.,
29.1 x 23.4 cm.
dated lower left

212 WEEPING HEAD
June 13, 1937 / Z IX: 47
pencil and coloured crayon,
11-1/2 x 9-1/4 in., 29.1 x 23.4 cm.
dated lower left

213 WEEPING HEAD
June 15, 1937 / not in Z
Pencil, coloured crayon and oil on
canvas, 21-5/8 x 18-1/8 in.,
54.8 x 46 cm.

214 WEEPING HEAD
June 15, 1937 / not in Z
pencil and gouache on cardboard,
4-5/8 x 3-1/2 in., 11.7 x 8.8 cm.
dated

215 WEEPING HEAD WITH
HANDKERCHIEF
June 22, 1937 / Z IX: 50
oil on canvas, 21-5/8 x 18-1/8 in.,
54.8 x 46 cm.

216 MOTHER WITH DEAD CHILD
June 22, 1937 / Z IX: 49
pencil, coloured crayon and oil on
canvas, 21-5/8 x 18-1/8 in.,
54.8 x 46 cm.

217 WEEPING WOMAN
July 2, 1937
etching, first state, 27-1/4 x 19-1/2 in.,
69.1 x 49.5 cm.

218 WEEPING WOMAN
July 22, 1937
etching, second state,
27-1/4 x 19-1/2 in., 69.1 x 49.5 cm.

219 WEEPING HEAD WITH
HANDKERCHIEF
July 4, 1937 / Z IX: 55
ink, 6 x 4-1/2 in., 15.2 x 11.4 cm.

220 WEEPING HEAD WITH
HANDKERCHIEF
July 6, 1937 / Z IX: 56
ink on tan paper, 10 x 6-3/4 in.,
25.3 x 17.1 cm.

221 MOTHER WITH DEAD CHILD
September 26, 1937 / Z IX: 69
oil on canvas, 51-1/4 x 76-3/4 in.,
130.1 x 194.8 cm.

222 WEEPING HEAD
October 12, 1937 / Z IX: 74
ink and pencil, 35-3/8 x 23 in.,
89.8 x 58.3 cm.

223 WEEPING HEAD WITH
HANDKERCHIEF
October 13, 1937 / not in Z
ink and oil on canvas,
21-5/8 x 18-1/8 in., 54.9 x 46 cm.

224 WEEPING WOMAN WITH
HANDKERCHIEF
October 17, 1937 / Z IX: 77
oil on canvas,
36-1/4 x 28-5/8 in., 92 x 72.6 cm.

225 GUERNICA: WOMAN WITH A
    HANDKERCHIEF

Paris, June 26, 1937 / Z IX: 51

oil on canvas, 21 x 17-1/2 in.,
53.3 x 44.4 cm.

signed 'A mon ami Zervos – Picasso'
top

Related Works: Z IX: 52

Provenance: Galerie Kate Perls,
Paris-New York; Perls Gallery, New
York; Thomas Mitchell, Los Angeles;
his gift to the museum 1955

Picasso Exhibitions: New York 1953,
Perls no. 12; Los Angeles 1961, UCLA
no. 28

lent by The Los Angeles County
Museum of Art
gift of Thomas Mitchell

After finishing the *Guernica* Picasso
made a number of independent studies
of the heads of women weeping as if
they were the official mourners for the
catastrophe which had taken place. If
one could imagine them exhibited
beside the *Guernica,* with their strong
colours against its large expanse of
grisaille, they would create an effect
of the most terrible sorrow to be heard
as well as seen.

This head with the eyes like tear-
drops and the cheeks creased by
weeping, still has the rounded forms
of the *Guernica* itself. In the later
studies, like the famous oil in the
collection of Roland Penrose (Z IX: 73)
and the watercolour in The Fogg Art
Museum (Z IX: 76), both done in
October, the forms become more
angular and the expression sharper.

226 COMBAT / LE COMBAT

October 10, 1937

etching and engraving,
15-5/8 x 19-7/16 in., 39.6 x 49.3 cm.

lent by The Museum of Modern Art,
New York
acquired through the Lillie P. Bliss
Bequest

227 DANCER WITH TAMBOURINE /
    FEMME AU TAMBOURIN

1938

etching and aquatint,
26-1/4 x 17-7/8 in., 66.6 x 45.3 cm.

lent by The Museum of Modern Art,
New York
acquired through the Lillie P. Bliss
Bequest

228 SEATED BOY/ENFANT ASSIS
October 9, 1939/not in Z

oil on canvas, 28-1/2 x 23-1/2 in.,
72.3 x 59.6 cm.

signed 'Picasso/9.10.39' lower right

Studies: Z X: 57-64

Provenance: G. David Thompson,
Pittsburg; acquired by present
owners 1960

Picasso Exhibitions: Los Angeles 1961,
UCLA no. 39

lent by Mr. and Mrs. Kirk Douglas

Uncertain about the war, which had broken out on September 3, 1939, and moody in his self-chosen isolation at Royan with his friend Sabartés and his mistress, Dora Maar, Picasso painted this cocky child. Undoubtedly he thought of the endearing portraits he had painted of his and Marie-Thérèse's daughter, Maïa, almost two years before, or even of the frightening *Child with a Cock* (Z IX: 109) he had painted one month later. There is in the spirited naughtiness also some reflection of the *Fishermen at Antibes* (Z IX: 316) which he had just painted that summer. Although his feet seem sound and, like a child's, exaggerately active, this small boy reminds one of Ribera's *Clubfoot* in the Louvre; the hair cut is similar and the smile is just as toothlessly indefatigable. Throughout the war Picasso was to suggest this spirit often; whether it was in a child taking his first step (Yale University, Z XIII: 36) or in a tomato plant continuing to grow, the emphasis was upon man's will to survive.

229 PORTRAIT OF DORA MAAR

Paris, March 27, 1939 / not in Z

oil on wood panel, 23-1/2 X 17-3/4 in., 59.6 X 45 cm.

signed 'Picasso/39' upper right and '27.3.39' on the back

Related Works: Z IX: 270-273, 276; Duncan p. 240, upper right and centre left

Provenance: Paul Rosenberg, New York; Private Collection, New York; acquired by S. Hahn 1962

lent by the Stephen Hahn Gallery

229

Dora Maar, who had become Picasso's mistress by 1937, seems to have been painted more times than any other human being by Picasso – and with greater freedom and greater range of expression. This portrait, which is one of the more conventional, is also one of the warmest and most romantic interpretations of Dora Maar. Her eyes are large, her long hair dark and her dress a rich red. At the same time apprehension and self-doubt are expressed by her mobile and tragic eyes.

230

Picasso must have painted this head of Dora Maar the day before they and Sabartés went to Paris that December. He had made several drawings on the fourth of September working toward portraits of this kind; one (Z X: 186) was particularly close, emphasizing the jaunty flowers on the hat and the sharp angles of the bob. His portraits of Dora Maar are often modish. We are conscious of chicly made clothes and hats and the fashionably long hair. But we are often conscious too of a frantic unhappiness as it is suggested in the picture's restlessness, the tensely smiling mouth and the irregular dark eyes.

231

In addition to Dora Maar and Sabartés at Royan, Picasso also had his Afghan hound, Kasbec, as a companion. Penrose (p. 278) has written of the dog, 'his profile with its sharp sensitive nose became traceable for several years among the human heads that Picasso invented. In fact Picasso has told me jokingly that his two most important models in these years before and during the Second World War were Kasbec and Dora Maar.' His existence can be sensed here in the bewildered expression as well as in the extended nose of the woman.

230 PORTRAIT OF DORA MAAR

Royan, December 4, 1939 / not in Z

oil on canvas, 16 x 13 in., 40.6 x 33 cm

signed 'Picasso/4.12.39' lower left

Sketches: Z X: 186, 187, 190

Provenance: Paul Rosenberg, New York; Perls Galleries, New York; G. David Thompson, Pittsburgh; Galerie Beyeler, Bâle, Switzerland; acquired by S. Hahn 1962

Picasso Exhibitions: Oslo 1955, no.185

lent by the Stephen Hahn Gallery

231 HEAD

Royan, March 3, 1940 / Z X: 374

oil on paper mounted on canvas, 25-1/2 x 18-1/2 in., 64.7 x 46.9 cm.

signed 'Picasso' in ink lower left and dated '3.3.40' lower right

Studies: Z X: 275

Related Works: Z X: 299, 300, 301

Provenance: Pierre Loeb, Paris; gift to the museum December 4, 1957

Picasso Exhibitions: New York 1962, MMA

lent by The Museum of Modern Art, New York

gift of Mr. and Mrs. Gordon Bunshaft

232 BLACK FIGURE ON A RED GROUND/
FEMME COUCHEE, FOND ROUGE

August 21, 1941/Z XI: 285

oil on canvas, 38 x 51 in.,
96.4 x 129.5 cm.

signed 'Picasso' lower left

Provenance: Kootz Gallery, New
York; acquired by present owner
1947

Picasso Exhibitions: Worcester 1962,
no. 5

lent from the Collection of
Himan Brown

Perhaps nothing could better express the desperate sense of boredom and imprisonment in German-occupied Paris than this reclining figure of Dora Maar. Even in the cushion she holds beneath her head, one of her large, soulful dark eyes is reflected. Picasso had made studies of reclining nude figures in the months before he painted this picture, but these do not give the same sense of desolation that this shapeless dress and shoes do. The relationship of Picasso and Dora Maar, which had never been serene, was now quite often strained and difficult and these strains and difficulties are usually apparent in his portraits of her. It is only occasionally in a painting like this that Picasso was moved to something very close to compassion for her.

233 SEATED WOMAN/FEMME ASSISE
DANS UN FAUTEUIL

September 1941/Z XI: 283

oil on canvas, 50-1/2 x 37-1/2 in.,
128.2 x 95.2 cm.

signed 'Picasso' upper left

Studies: Z XI: 280-282

Provenance: Kootz Gallery, New
York; acquired by the museum 1950

Picasso Exhibitions: Paris 1946,
Carré no. VI

lent by The Currier Gallery of Art

Although only painted in the month
after the *Black Figure on a Red Ground*
(no. 232) this seated portrait of Dora
Maar seems quite different in character,
if equally unhappy. She has assumed
the fashionable dress and sleek groom-
ing with which Picasso normally inter-
preted her – and she has also assumed
a spiney defensiveness in her angularity
and the way she withdraws back into
the chair. Even the colour has a certain
challenging brightness. Like many of
the wartime pictures we are made
conscious of the enclosure of the room.
There are preparatory drawings for this
and other rooms which makes it apparent that the perspective, which any
could consider arbitrary and some
whimsically casual, was actually arrived
at after some analysis and revision.

234 RECLINING NUDE/NU COUCHE

September 30, 1942/Z XII: 156

oil on canvas, 51-1/4 x 76-3/4 in., 130.1 x 194.8 cm.

signed 'Picasso' lower left and dated on stretcher

Provenance: Galerie Louise Leiris; acquired by present owner August 1956

Picasso Exhibitions: Brussels 1946, no. 14; Milan 1953, no. 98; Paris 1955, Décoratifs no. 103; Münich 1956; London 1960, Arts Council no. 169; Worcester 1962, no. 6; New York 1962, Tribute, Staempfli no. 2

lent from the Collection of Victor W. Ganz

This large and important painting sums up Picasso's experiences during the occupation. It is dreary, without the relief of colour or any sensuality in the reclining figure of the female nude. The room in which she lies is bleak and confining, her cot as restless as her body. And if the woman (presumably Dora Maar) is sleeping, her body in its twisted angularity, reveals how tormented that sleep must be. Although the colour and the forms hark back to analytic cubism their austerity here seems intended for a more emotional than intellectual purpose; one suspects that as much as in his *Still Life with Sausages* (Z XI: 112), painted the year before and in the same collection, Picasso wanted to paint 'a real Philip II picture.' (See New York 1962, Tribute, Introduction by John Richardson.)

235 WOMAN IN GREEN / FEMME EN VERT

1943 / Z XIII: 49

oil on canvas, 51-1/4 x 38-1/8 in.,
130.1 x 96.8 cm.

signed 'Picasso' upper left

Provenance: Kootz Gallery, New York

Picasso Exhibitions: New York 1957,
MMA p. 87; Philadelphia 1958,
no. 211; London 1960, Arts Council
no. 174; New York 1962, Tribute,
Staempfli no. 7; Worcester 1962, no. 8

lent by Miss Ciannait Sweeney

To Be Exhibited In Toronto Only

As the circumstances of the war seemed
to become more oppressive Picasso
enlarged his figures in relation to the
spaces they filled; this woman in con-
sequence seems terrifyingly monumental. In spite of the pathetic touches of
civilization, like the rickrack braided
collar and the golden buttons, and the
propriety with which she sits with her
hands folded primly in her lap, those
hands are anatomically grotesque,
the movements through her body and
dress are restless, and yet confined,
and her face, with the Afghan hound's
nose, is twisted, haunted and distracted.
The human elements in it seem subord-
inated to an uncomprehending animal
fear, which the boldness and the
richness of the colour emphasize.

WOMAN BATHING HER RIGHT FOOT/
FEMME SE LAVANT

WOMAN WASHING HER FEET/
FEMME SE LAVANT

NUDE AND WOMAN WASHING HER
FEET/NU ET FEMME SE LAVANT
LES PIEDS

236 WOMAN BATHING HER RIGHT
     FOOT/ FEMME SE LAVANT
     May 6, 1944/ Z XIII: 291
     pencil, 19-7/8 x 15-1/8 in.,
     50.4 x 38.4 cm.
     signed '6 mai 44/Picasso' upper left
     Related Works: Z XIII: 273, 290,
     316-319, 323, 325

Provenance: Curt Valentin; willed by
him to the museum 1955

Picasso Exhibitions: New York 1952,
Valentin no. 34; New York 1957,
MMA p. 90; Philadelphia 1958, no.
213; Worcester 1962, no. 11

lent by The Art Institute of Chicago
bequest of Curt Valentin

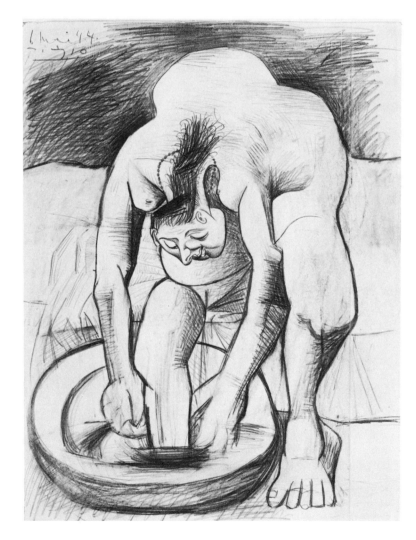

236

In 1943 and 1944, as if he could no longer stand the claustrophobia of his studio, Picasso wandered out into Paris and made drawings of the city (Z XIII: 59-62) and particularly of the people he saw in its parks (Z XIII: 186-188, 230). He seems to have been enchanted by the sight of mothers leaning over to pick up their babies, sometimes to nurse them, and he made sketches of them reaching over to the ground (Z XIII: 16, 17, 18, 113-120, 231). It may have been the memory of that movement and the pleasure in its sheer domesticity that persuaded him to draw a nude in the same position at the equally domestic, if more plebian, activity of washing her feet. The result is a drawing of remarkable earthiness and power.

237

For a few months Picasso seems to have found as much pleasure in the nude bather as the Impressionist painter Degas had done toward the end of the 19th century. He explored various ways of handling this theme and, in this drawing, used brush and ink to make a more fluid, luminous version of her. Although he depends upon a play of light and dark like Rembrandt's chiaroscuro, the brilliance of the light dominates any somberness in the shadows.

In one of the first photographs taken of Picasso after the Liberation of Paris in 1944 (by Robert Capa for *Life*: see *The Museum of Modern Art Bulletin*, January 1945, p. 5) the right of this canvas peers out behind a pile of others; the persistent image of the woman washing her feet was now unconfined. This composition, which seems to be the conclusion of all the studies Picasso had made of this figure, combines her with an indolent and very much elongated female companion who lies nude upon a bed. The scene is certainly one of apathy and boredom – but painted with the kind of detachment and humour Picasso's wartime works until this time had seldom revealed. It is possible that his knowledge of the invasion of France by allied troops gave Picasso this optimistic and lighthearted approach to the predicament he was sharing with his fellow Parisians.

237 WOMAN WASHING HER FEET / FEMME SE LAVANT

July 10, 1944 / Z XIII: 323

brush and ink, 20 x 13-1/4 in., 50.7 x 33.6 cm.

signed '10 juillet/44/VII/Picasso' upper left

Related Works: Z XIII: 273, 290, 291, 316-319, 325

Provenance: acquired by the museum 1953

Picasso Exhibitions: New York 1957, MMA p. 90; Philadelphia 1958, no. 214

lent by The Museum of Modern Art, New York Purchase Fund

238 NUDE AND WOMAN WASHING HER FEET / NU ET FEMME SE LAVANT LES PIEDS

August 18, 1944 / Z XIII: 273

oil on canvas, 38 x 51 in., 96.5 x 129.5 cm.

signed 'Picasso' lower right

Studies: Z XIII: 290, 291, 316-319, 323, 325

Provenance: Kootz Gallery, New York; acquired by present owner 1956

Picasso Exhibitions: Brussels 1946, no. 21; New York 1947, Kootz; Milan 1953, no. 109; New York 1956, Kootz; Worcester 1962, no. 12

lent by Mrs. George S. Mack

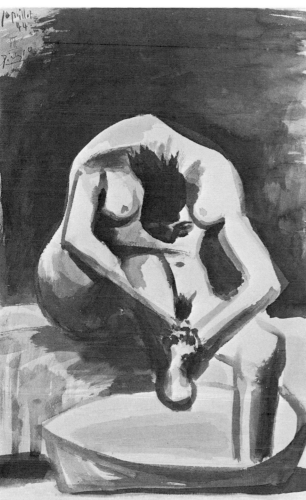

242 FAUN/LE FAUNE SUR FOND BLANC

Antibes 1946

oil on canvas, 25-3/4 x 19-3/4 in.,
65.3 x 50.1 cm.

signed 'Picasso' lower left

Provenance: not given

lent by the Perls Galleries

239 PASTORALE

1945

etching (printed in green),
10-11/16 x 13-15/16 in., 27.1 x 35.3 cm.

lent by The Museum of Modern Art,
New York
acquired through the Lillie P. Bliss
Bequest

240 HEAD OF A YOUNG BOY/
TETE DE JEUNE GARCON

November 7, 1945/M I: 8

lithograph, 12-1/4 x 9-3/8 in.,
31 x 23.7 cm.

lent by Mr. William S. Lieberman

241 HEAD OF FRANCOISE

June 14, 1946/M I: 47

lithograph, 24-7/8 x 18-15/16 in.,
63 x 48 cm.

lent from the Collection of
Walter Carsen

Picasso's happiness at Antibes the autumn of 1946 seemed to have been the result of one fortunate event after another – the Liberation of Paris in 1944, the acquisition of the young painter, Françoise Gillot, as his mistress, and the loan of the museum of Antibes, the Palais Grimaldi, as a place to paint. In that beautiful and ancient Mediterranean city Picasso evoked his own classical mythology, peopling his canvases with fauns, centaurs and nude women who were far more light-hearted than any he had imagined in his earlier classical periods. His painting, like this head of a faun, was often spiritedly abbreviated, here even suggesting it had been done with a child's crayon. This was not the naïvete of senility, however; over the complacently smiling face Picasso drew angular forms to suggest self-doubts even in one of his Arcadian figures.

243 PORTRAIT OF FRANCOISE GILLOT

April 2, 1947

oil on canvas, 39-1/4 x 31-1/2 in.,
99.6 x 80 cm.

signed 'Picasso' upper left and
dated '2-4-47' on the back

Related Works: see Boeck & Sabartés
p. 329

Provenance: Kootz Gallery,
New York

Picasso Exhibitions: New York 1948,
Kootz; Worcester 1962, no. 23

lent by Miss Katharine Ordway

Picasso's affection for Françoise Gillot,
which he had expressed in his serene
lithographs of her (see no. 241),
also appears in these lighthearted and
heraldic transformations of her figure
in 1947. She belongs to the joyous
mythological world he had been
painting for the museum at Antibes, and
he also compliments her metaphorically
by comparing her, as he often did, to
both the sun and a flower.

248 SEATED WOMAN/
FEMME ASSISE DANS UN FAUTEUIL

Vallauris 1948-1949

oil on canvas, 39-1/2 x 32 in.,
100.3 x 81.2 cm.

signed 'Piccaso' lower right and dated
'29/12/48-1/1/49' on the back

Provenance: Galerie Louise Leiris;
acquired by present owner 1959

Picasso Exhibitions: São Paulo 1954,
no. 48; Paris 1955, Décoratifs no. 115;
München 1955

lent by Mrs. Phyllis B. Lambert

As M. Maurice Jardot has pointed
out (Paris 1955, Décoratifs no. 115)
this painting belongs to a series in a
calligraphic style which culminates in
Picasso's most nearly abstract painting,
the *Kitchen* of 1948, which he has kept
in his own collection (see Duncan
p. 244). Since the woman – clearly
pregnant Françoise – is seated in a
room, it is natural to compare her with
the two wartime seated portraits of
Dora Maar in the exhibition (nos. 229
and 230). Surprisingly the interpretation
of Françoise seems pettier and more
vicious – decorative and colourful
though the work may be. The fluctua-
tions in Picasso's feelings for Françoise
may be traced in some lithographs he
made of her that same winter
(see M II: 133-138).

138

244 CENTAUR AND BACCHANTE
February 2, 1947 / M I: 62
lithograph, 21-5/16 x 18-15/16 in.,
54 x 48 cm.
lent anonymously

245 DAVID AND BATHSHEBA
(after CRANACH)
March 30, 1947 / M II: 109 iv
lithograph, 25-1/4 x 19-5/16 in.,
64 x 49 cm.
lent by Mr. and Mrs. Dion A. Bowman

246 BLACK HEAD / FIGURE NOIRE
Vallauris, November 20, 1948 / M 126
lithograph on zinc,
25-5/16 x 19-9/16 in., 64.2 x 49.6 cm.
lent by The Museum of Modern Art,
New York
Mrs. John D. Rockefeller, Jr.,
Purchase Fund

247 WOMAN IN AN ARMCHAIR NO. 4 /
FEMME AU FAUTEUIL
Vallauris, January 3, 1949 / M II: 137
lithograph, 27-1/2 x 21-1/2 in.,
69.8 x 54.5 cm.
lent by The Museum of Modern Art,
New York
Curt Valentin Bequest

249 PREGNANT WOMAN /
FEMME ENCEINTE
Vallauris 1950
bronze, 44-1/4 in. high, 112.3 cm.
not signed
lent by The Museum of Modern Art,
New York
gift of Mrs. Bertram Smith

This figure of a pregnant woman seems like a good-humoured fertility totem and a sign of the pleasure Françoise had given Picasso in presenting him with children when he was sixty-six and sixty-eight. Picasso had begun to make sculpture again when he moved to Vallauris – the pottery making town which he adopted and helped prosper with his ceramics.

250 HEAD OF A WOMAN/
TETE DE FEMME

Vallauris 1951

bronze, 21-1/2 in. high, 54.5 cm.

lent from the Collection of
Joseph H. Hirshhorn

In the limiting form of the diamond-
shaped head of this piece of sculpture
Picasso managed to suggest, with
extraordinary human perception and
detachment, the wistful sadness of the
young woman who had born him his
two youngest children.

251 PALOMA AND DOLL
(BLACK BACKGROUND)/
PALOMA ET SA POUPEE
SUR FOND NOIR

Vallauris, December 14, 1952/
M III: 229

lithograph, 27-3/4 x 21-3/4 in.,
70.4 x 55.1 cm.

lent by The Museum of Modern Art,
New York
Curt Valentin Bequest

252 SEATED NUDE/NU ASSIS

Vallauris, July 1953/not in Z

oil on canvas, 15-1/4 x 37-3/4 in.,
130.1 x 95.8 cm.

signed 'Picasso/July 1953' lower left

Provenance: Galerie Louise Leiris,
Paris; Curt Valentin, New York

Picasso Exhibitions: New York 1953,
Valentin no. 8; New York 1962,
Tribute, Cordier-Warren no.1

lent by The City Art Museum of
St. Louis
gift of Mr. and Mrs. Joseph
Pulitzer, Jr.

This monumental nude, with its echoes
of analytical cubism, has the subdued
palette which the town of Vallauris
sometimes seems to have inspired in
Picasso, particularly when he was aware
of Françoise's unhappiness with him.
This painting is a dignified and even
heroic interpretation of her hestitations.
He had begun by imagining her as a
nymph in his own imaginary and
playful classical world, and had ended
by seeing her as a figure who could
have taken her place in the sternest
tragedies of the Greeks.

253 WOMAN SEATED,
BLUE BACKGROUND /
FEMME ASSISE FOND AZUR

Vallauris 1953

oil on canvas, 36 x 28-1/2 in.,
91.4 x 72.3 cm.

signed 'Picasso' lower left

Provenance: Galerie Louise Leiris;
acquired by present owners 1953

lent by Mr. and Mrs. John David Eaton

This painting belongs to a group of
portraits Picasso painted in March
1953 which may have been the last for
which Francoise posed. With her long
hair now sternly drawn back from her
face in a bun she seems more innately
serious than she had in his earlier
portraits of her.

This version is one of the most decorative and serene although there is
some malice (Picasso's, one suspects)
in the left profile.

254 WOMAN WITH A DOG/
LA FEMME AU CHIEN

Vallauris 1953

oil on panel, 31-15/16 x 39-7/16 in.,
81 x 100 cm.

signed 'Picasso' lower right and
'Vallauris/8.3.53' on the back

Picasso Exhibitions: Milan 1953, no.
173; London 1954, Lefevre no. 10;
Lucerne 1961, Rosengart

lent by Galerie Rosengart, Lucerne

It was probably the departure of Françoise in 1953 which stimulated Picasso to paint scenes of the most terrible predatory viciousness, one, for example, of a cat eating a cock. Since his love for dogs is thoroughly established, it can be presumed that Picasso identified himself in this work with the helpless, terrified and colourless animal caught in the grips of the woman in her peacock-coloured dress. The intensity of the work is increased by the intensity of the colour, which does not prevent one from absorbing, however, the horrifyingly tender expression on the woman's face.

255 THE SHADOW ON THE WOMAN/
L'OMBRE DE L'ARTISTE

Vallauris, December 29, 1953

oil on canvas, 51-1/4 x 38-1/4 in.,
130.1 x 97.1 cm.

signed 'Picasso' lower left and dated
'29.12.53' on the back

Related Works: Duncan p. 183

Provenance: Galerie Rosengart,
Lucerne

lent from the Collection of
Ayala and Sam Zacks

Picasso has kept a version of this work
which he explained to Douglas Duncan
(Duncan p. 183), 'It was our bedroom.
See my shadow? I'd just turned from
the window – *now* do you see my
shadow and the sunlight falling onto
the bed and across the floor? See the
toy cart on the dresser [not in this
version], and the little vase over the
fireplace? They're from Sicily and still
around the house.' Picasso's feeling for
the domestic setting and the drama
with which he placed his translucent
shadow over the nude figure of the
woman may have revealed some nostalgia for his life with Françoise.

256 FIGURES IN A GARDEN FROM A
WINDOW/FIGURES DANS UN
JARDIN

Vallauris 1953-1954

oil on canvas, 59-1/4 x 38-3/4 in.,
150.4 x 98.4 cm.

signed 'Picasso' upper right

Related Works: Duncan p. 180

Provenance: James Wise, Geneva;
Eric Estorick, London; acquired by
present owners September 2, 1957

Picasso Exhibitions: Santa Barbara
1960; Los Angeles 1961, UCLA no. 41

lent by Mr. and Mrs. David E. Bright

To Be Exhibited In Toronto Only

It is difficult to avoid considering a
painting like this as a form of auto-
biography. Picasso painted himself as a
scarcely distinguishable dark figure,
identifiable by the few stripes of his
maillot and the brush in his hand,
working with purposefulness and
melancholy while behind him through
the window we can see the brilliant
and decorative garden and his four-
year-old daughter, Paloma, playing
with her new Christmas toy.

257 DRAWING FOR THE
HUMAN COMEDY
Vallauris, January 29, 1954
watercolour, 9-1/2 x 12-1/2 in.,
24 x 31.7 cm.
signed 'Picasso' lower right
Provenance: Galerie Louise Leiris;
acquired by present owners April
1962
lent by Mr. and Mrs. T. M. Sterling

258 DANCE OF THE BANDERILLAS/
LA DANSE DES BANDERILLES
Vallauris, February 14, 1954/M III: 248
lithograph, 18-9/16 x 25 in.,
47.1 x 63.4 cm.
lent by The Museum of Modern Art,
New York
Larry Aldrich Fund

259 THE THREE WOMEN AND THE
TOREADOR/LES TROIS FEMMES ET
LE TORERO
Vallauris, February 17, 1954/M III: 251
lithograph, 19-3/4 x 25-5/8 in.,
50 x 65 cm.
lent by Mr. and Mrs. Bion A. Bowman

260 TORSO OF A WOMAN/
TORSE DE FEMME
1954
aquatint, 35-3/4 x 25-3/16 in.,
90.7 x 64 cm.
lent by Mr. M. F. Feheley

261 HEAD OF A SATYR/TETE DE SATYRE

1954 ?

coloured crayon, 12-1/2 x 9-3/4 in.
(sight), 31.7 x 24.7 cm.

signed 'Picasso' upper right

Provenance: E. Gordon, New York;
acquired by present owners 1961

lent by Dr. and Mrs. John D.
Constable

During the spring and summer of 1954
Picasso, who found himself exceedingly
lonely and restless, took a great deal of
pleasure in painting a blond pony-
tailed girl called Sylvette David. As John
Richardson has pointed out (New York
1962, Tribute, the Fifties), 'In the final
portraits of Sylvette the features subtly
changed their cast; this is because the
artist had fallen in love with the young
and beautiful Jacqueline Roque and, as
always, had begun to see other people
in terms of his beloved.' Picasso
lengthened the neck of Sylvette, made
her features more austere and adult
and pulled up her hair like a helmet so
that she seems a French version of
Nefretete, whom Jacqueline Roque did,
in fact, resemble. Something of the
Riviera gamin survives this idealization
however.

262 SYLVETTE
1954

oil on canvas, 28 x 23 in., 71 x 58.3 cm.

signed 'Picasso' upper left

Provenance: Berggruen & Cie, Paris;
anonymous gift to the museum 1959

Picasso Exhibitions: Paris 1954, la
Pensée française II no. 48

lent from the Collection Washington
University, St. Louis

263 THE WOMEN OF ALGIERS/
LES FEMMES D'ALGER

Paris, February 14, 1955

oil on canvas, 44-7/8 x 57-1/2 in.,
114 x 146 cm.

signed 'Picasso' upper right and
dated on the back

Provenance: Galerie Louise Leiris;
acquired by present owner June 1956

Picasso Exhibitions: Paris 1955,
Décoratifs no.127/0; Münich 1955;
New York 1957, MMA p. 109;

Philadelphia 1958, no. 225; London
1960, Arts Council no.196; New York
1962, Tribute, Cordier-Warren no.18

lent from the Collection of
Victor W. Ganz

Picasso has said himself that it was the resemblance of the crouching figure at the hookah in Delacroix's *Femmes d'Alger* in the Louvre to Jacqueline Roque that inspired him to paint fifteen free translations of it. He returned to Paris that winter with Jacqueline, settled in his studio on the rue des Grands-Augustins, banished any reproductions or photographs of the Delacroix from his presence and began on December 13th to make his own versions of this theme. The final and most flamboyant is in this exhibition.

It is difficult even to speculate how much Picasso was interpreting Delacroix, how much the possibilities of the subject itself, how much his feelings for Jacqueline; all one can say is that it culminates in a painting of sheer, aggressive splendour. The series does reveal, however, how much Picasso was concerned with experiencing space, and in some of the grisaille versions, in particular, with analytical cubism as his guide. In this version lines, colours, bodies thrust us joyously back and forth through the space, even if we reach some peace in the seated figure with the hookah, presumably a portrait of Jacqueline.

THE STUDIO/L'ATELIER

HEAD OF A WOMAN/TETE DE FEMME

SEATED WOMAN/FEMME ASSISE

264　THE STUDIO/L'ATELIER

Cannes 1956

oil on canvas, 44-15/16 x 57-1/2 in., 114 x 146 cm.

signed 'Picasso' upper right and '2.4.56.III/8.4.56' on the back

Related Works: see Paris 1957, Leiris

Picasso Exhibitions: Paris 1957, Leiris no. 24; Lucerne 1961, Rosengart

lent by Galerie Rosengart, Lucerne

In 1956 Picasso painted a group of pictures which were inspired by the combination of Jacqueline Roque's beautiful profile and the villa, la Californie, which he had just bought at Cannes. Jacqueline sits quietly and somewhat sadly gazing at a canvas on the easel of the interior of la Californie, for Picasso continues to juxtapose spaces as imaginatively as he had in the *Femmes d'Alger*. There is an expansiveness to the painting and a subtlety in colour which emphasizes how deeply Picasso felt about the seated Jacqueline.

For a discussion of the group of paintings to which this belongs see John Richardson, 'Picasso's Ateliers and other recent works', *The Burlington Magazine,* June 1957, pp. 183 to 193.

265

When the photographer, Duncan, visited Picasso in 1957 he found him preoccupied, busy on a series of heads, in paint and in construction, of which this is one. These portraits seem harsh interpretations of Jacqueline, and psychologically complex, after his early idealized portraits of her. The sense of alarm, which Picasso suggests perhaps most potently in this one, may have been the result of the illness from which we are told (New York 1962, Tribute, the Fifties) Jacqueline was suffering. Like each of the portraits of Jacqueline, whom Picasso was to marry the next year, it is painted with a complete sense of identification and sympathy.

266

In this painting of a nude there is a dramatic gloom for which Jacqueline's illness may in part account. It is, nevertheless, an exceedingly human work, with an emphasis, in the very directness with which it is painted, upon the uncertainty mankind often feels. Picasso seems to have gone far beyond any portrait of Jacqueline into a sympathetic investigation of a human problem with which she might or might not be identified. It was painted exactly a month after Picasso and she married.

265 HEAD OF A WOMAN/
TETE DE FEMME

Cannes 1957

oil on canvas, 31-15/16 x 25-5/8 in.,
81 x 65 cm.

signed 'Picasso' upper right and dated
'29.6.57' on the back

Related Works: see David Douglas
Duncan, *The Private World of Pablo
Picasso*, New York: Ridge Press,
1958, section V

Picasso Exhibitions: Lucerne 1961,
Rosengart

lent by Galerie Rosengart, Lucerne

266 SEATED WOMAN/FEMME ASSISE

Cannes, April 2, 1958

oil on canvas, 51 x 38 in.,
129.5 x 96.5 cm.

signed 'Picasso' upper left

Provenance: acquired from Picasso
1959

lent by Mr. and Mrs. Samuel M. Kootz

267 SEATED WOMAN / FEMME ASSISE

Cannes, February 10, 1959

oil on canvas, 45-1/2 x 35 in.,
115.5 x 88.8 cm.

signed 'Picasso' upper left and dated
'10.2.59' on the back

Provenance: Galerie Louise Leiris;
acquired by the gallery 1959

Picasso Exhibitions: New York 1959,
Saidenberg no. 17

lent by the Saidenberg Gallery,
New York

At the time that Picasso painted this
picture he was in the process of
taking up residence in the château at
Vauvenargues, near Aix-en-Provence,
which he had acquired the September
before. Maurice Jardot has written
(Paris 1962, Leiris) of this place, 'Le site
a de la grandeur mais il est sévère,
comme le château lui-même. A son
ami Kahnweiler qui le met en garde
contre la tristesse du lieu, Picasso
répond tranquillement qu'il n'a pas
peur de cela, puisqu'il est Espagnol.'
This desire for austerity can be found
in figures like this woman in which
there are also the most overt references
to equally austere primitive art. The
work gains in sculptural power from
its somber brown palette and also
from the forceful contrast between
the gigantic hands and the small head
in space. Awesome and strange as
this figure is, she does arouse some
sympathy in us for her apparent
bewilderment.

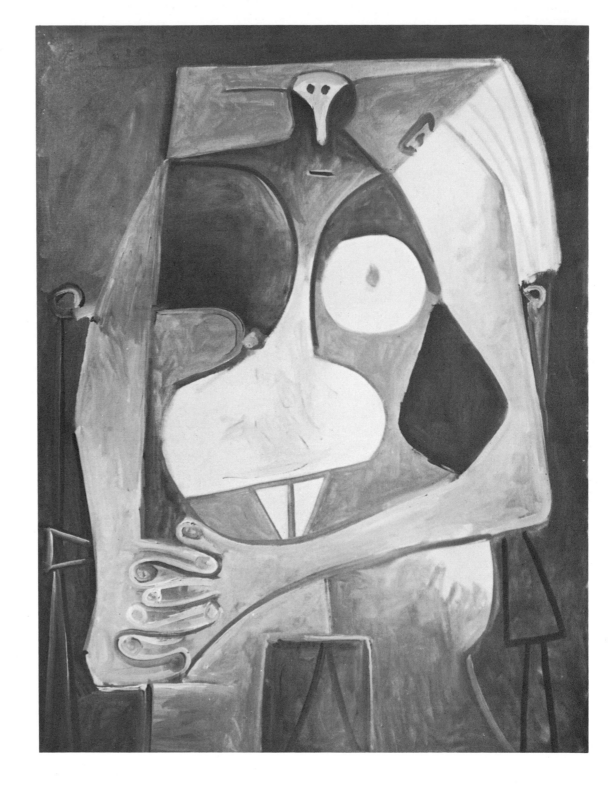

268 WOMAN SEATED / FEMME ASSISE

Cannes, February 1-March 9, 1959/
Duncan p. 258, upper left

oil on canvas, 57-1/2 x 45 in.,
146 x 114.2 cm.

signed 'Picasso' upper left and dated
14.2.59/18.2.59/19.22/8.-9.-3.59
on the back

Provenance: Kootz Gallery, New
York; acquired by present owner
October 1963

Picasso Exhibitions: New York 1962,
Kootz

lent from the Collection of
Victor W. Ganz

It is possible that Picasso's greatest
theme since the war has been the
female nude, dazzling though the
interludes of his series after other
painters' pictures may be. At the same
time these nudes are so personal that
they often seem portraits, as this one
does of Jacqueline, and so expressive
that their nudity appears an indication
of intimacy rather than an end in
itself. In this painting, Picasso exaggerated the size of the feet and emphasized that exaggeration by the smaller
shoes beside them on the floor; this
seems to increase their restlessness. In
the same way the gigantic hands seem
intended to emphasize their anguish.
And ungainly as the taut body is, it
culminates in the magnificent eyes of
Jacqueline's moving and beautiful head.

The degree of domesticity in this
painting is suggested by the shoes, of
course, but also by the key at the left
which recalls the keys in some of his
Dinard paintings of 1928 but seems to
lead to nothing more enigmatic than a
small cupboard or refrigerator with a
milk bottle on the top. The figure itself,
which does dominate over such trivia,
is dramatic and universal.

THE ARM/LE BRAS

NUDE ON DIVAN/NU SUR DIVAN

HEAD OF A WOMAN/
TETE DE FEMME

269 THE ARM/LE BRAS
Cannes, March 15, 1959
bronze, 22-3/4 in. high, 57.7 cm.
dated '15.3.59'
lent from the Collection of
Joseph H. Hirshhorn

This arm, which is clearly Picasso's own, is strong and simple, its fingers stretched forth without pretension or affectation as if to feel its strength and welcome the world around it. Picasso seems to have created a symbol, after having come to some understanding of the world and himself, of the way he can live with some assurance within it. He does not demand but is firm, he is responsive but steady, rugged but disciplined, realistic but imaginative. And above all he is confident, courageous and free.

Periodically Picasso would turn back to the stooping figure of a woman which he had studied most intensively in 1944 and which he was to make an important secondary figure in his translations of Manet's *Déjeuner sur l'herbe* (see nos. 272-274); one such occasion was his painting of this monumental nude with the free distortions and flattening of parts of the body. The face seems young and ingenuous as she confronts her female self with some surprise.

Although this head is the result of the confrontation of two highly mobile profiles which seem to meet with that surprise Picasso had revealed in the meeting of the conscious and the unconscious self as early as 1925, they are combined together so skillfully and dominated so completely by the two similar dark eyes and the unifying head of hair that the suggestion of a single head is perfectly convincing. Jacqueline's features seem filled with great dramatic intensity.

270 NUDE ON DIVAN/NU SUR DIVAN

February 3, 1960/Duncan p. 258
lower left

oil on canvas, 77 x 54-1/2 in.,
195.4 x 138.4 cm.

signed 'Picasso' lower right and dated
'3.2.60' on the back

Picasso Exhibitions: New York 1962,
Kootz

lent by the Samuel M. Kootz Gallery,
New York

271 HEAD OF A WOMAN/
TETE DE FEMME

November 28-30, 1960

oil on canvas, 25-1/2 x 20-1/2 in.,
64.7 x 52 cm.

signed 'Picasso' upper left and dated
'28.11.60' and '30.11.60' on the back

Provenance: Kootz Gallery, New York

lent by Mr. and Mrs. Leonard S. Field

272 LE DEJEUNER SUR L'HERBE

Mougins, July 16, 1961/ Cooper no. 112

oil on canvas, 34-15/16 x 45-9/16 in.,
88.7 x 115.7 cm.

signed 'Picasso' lower right and
'N. D. de Vie 16.7.61' on the back

Related Works: see Cooper

Picasso Exhibitions: Paris 1962, Leiris,
Déjeuner no. 17; Lucerne 1963,
Rosengart

lent by Galerie Rosengart, Lucerne

In August 1959 Picasso made his first drawings after Manet's *Déjeuner sur l'herbe* in the Louvre; he continued to make variations upon this picture for the next two years. Three elements seem to have fascinated Picasso in the nineteenth century painting. One was the coolness and greenness of the glade which in his twenty-three painted versions he varied, but kept fresh and full of light. Another was the stooping figure in the background (usually nude and leaning over to pick a flower) which Picasso frequently drew alone. Both this figure and the green seem constant and inevitable – but against their relative serenity there is the third element which preoccupied Picasso – the conversation which is taking place between the man at the right, whom Mr. Cooper aptly calls *Le Causeur,* and the female figure at the left. In Picasso's first painting of the *Déjeuner,* the woman remains as limpidly and beautifully indifferent to the point the man is making with his outstretched arm as the nude does in Manet's painting – but, as the thrust of that arm varies from beseeching to admonition and the expression on the *Causeur's* face from fanaticism to indifference, she also changes. Sometimes she is an adorable, plump nude; at other times as exotic and dignified as Jacqueline. And with all these variations the dialogue continues, occasionally with the overtones of a seduction, often purely philosophic, and sometimes as strange and enigmatic as an ancient mystery.

273 LE DÉJEUNER SUR L'HERBE

Mougins, August 10, 1961 / Cooper
no. 152

oil on canvas, 36-1/8 x 28-3/4 in.,
91.7 x 73 cm.

dated '10/8/61 I' on the back

Related Works: see Cooper

Picasso Exhibitions: Paris 1962, Leiris,
Déjeuner no. 25

lent by Picasso Arts Inc., New York

In the version (no. 272) which was painted on July 16, 1961, and therefore toward the end of the series, the second male of Manet's painting, whom Picasso did sometimes include as a debonnaire spectator and, in the versions closest to this, as lounging indifferently on the grass and reading, is eliminated completely so that the emphasis could be on the two protagonists. The nude, who in many of the paintings is an urbane and assured young woman impressed by the dominant *Causeur,* is here a strange, hypnotized creature who seems to swell as she responds to the mysterious and sylvan man before her. As a result, the picture, as Mr. Cooper has written (p. 21), 'has a nightmarish intensity.'

About the stage in the painting of the *Déjeuners,* of which no. 273 is part, Mr. Cooper has written (p. 22), 'The third phase in the evolution of the *Déjeuners* is represented by six large and striking canvases – executed between 30th July and 10th August – which are phantasmagoric in their effect. The pictorial conception has here undergone a complete metamorphosis and no trace remains of either a peaceful Sunday afternoon outing, a picnic or even a *Baignade.* . . . Nothing here is stable, nothing seems quite real. We have been transported to a dream world. People change size with terrifying rapidity.'

1881 October 25	born in Malaga, Spain to José Ruiz Blasco, teacher of art, and Maria Picasso Lopez	
1891	family moved to Corunna (Galicia)	
1895	family moved to Barcelona	
1896	Picasso passed the entrance examination for the Provincial School of Fine Arts called "La Lonja" where his father taught	
	exhibited *First Communion* at Municipal exhibition, Barcelona	
1897	first exhibition of Picasso's work at Els Quatre Gats, Barcelona	
	first article on his work, review of exhibition by Rodríquez Codolá in *la Vanguardia*	
September or October	went to Madrid	
October	passed entrance examinations for advanced study at the Royal Academy of San Fernando	
	won honorable mention at the National Exhibition at Royal Academy of San Fernando with *Science and Charity*	
1898 spring	succumbed to scarlet fever, returned to Barcelona	
summer	convalescence at Horta de San Juan (Horta de Ebro)	
autumn	returned to Barcelona	
1900 September	went to Paris, sold three canvases to dealer Berthe Weill	
December 1	returned to Spain	
1901 January	moved to Madrid, became art editor for new, short-lived periodical, *Arte Joven*	
May	left Madrid for Barcelona	
	exhibited pastels at Sala Parés, Barcelona	
May or June	left for Paris	
June	Utrillo published an article on Picasso's work in *Pel e Pluma*	
June	first Paris exhibition at Vollard (with another painter called Iturrino); exhibition was criticized but Picasso won support of critic Gustave Coquiot and friendship of Max Jacob	
	now signs pictures only by his mother's name "Picasso"; formerly used "P. R(uiz) Picasso"	

BEGINNING OF THE BLUE PERIOD

1902 January	returned to Barcelona where he spent most of the year	
October 3	returned to Paris, shared hotel room with Max Jacob	
November 15	opening of group show at Berthe Weill's gallery in which Picasso exhibited	
1903 early	returned to Barcelona for more than a year	
	painted *La Vie*, The Cleveland Museum of Art	
1904 April	returned to Paris for good, settled in the "Bateau Lavoir", 13 rue de Ravignan	

BEGINNING OF THE ROSE PERIOD

1905	Fernande Olivier began to live with Picasso	
May	Guillaume Apollinaire met Picasso and wrote an article on him in *la Plume*	
summer	trip to Holland	
	met Leo and Gertrude Stein; Russian collector Shchukine began to buy his works; may have met Matisse this autumn	
	painted the *Saltimbanques*, National Gallery of Art, Washington	
1906 summer	Gosol (Spain)	
	met Kahnweiler, who was to become his dealer, and painters Braque and Vlaminck	
autumn	began work on the *Demoiselles d'Avignon*	

PROTO-CUBISM

1907 spring	finished work on the *Demoiselles d'Avignon*	
1908 end of the summer	La Rue des Bois (Oise) with Fernande	
	Rousseau Banquet	
November	Braque had an exhibition at Kahnweiler's of works he had painted that summer at l'Estaque; in a review of it in the November 14 *Gil Blas* Louis Vauxcelles spoke of the cubes, thus christening 'cubism'	
1909 summer	Horta de San Juan (Horta de Ebro) with Fernande	
autumn	moved to 11 blvd. Clichy	

ANALYTICAL CUBISM

1910 summer	Cadaqués (Spain) with Fernande and Derain	
1911 summer	Céret (French Pyrenees) with Braque and Fernande	
1912 spring	end of liaison with Fernande	
	Marcel Humbert (Eva) became his mistress	
spring	Avignon with Eva	
May 18	went with Eva to Céret, where Braque was staying, for one month	
June	went with Eva to Sorgues where Braque also stayed	
October	returned to Paris and moved to 242 blvd. Raspail	

SYNTHETIC CUBISM

1913 summer	Céret with Braque, Juan Gris and Eva	
	father died in Barcelona	
	took a studio on 5 bis rue Schoelcher	
1914 summer	Avignon with Braque, Derain and Eva	
1915 December	Eva died	
1916	moved to 22 rue Victor Hugo, Montrouge	
1917 February	to Rome with Jean Cocteau, did scenery and costumes for *La Parade*, met Stravinsky and the dancer Olga Koklova	
	visited Florence, Naples, Pompeii	
May 17	*La Parade* opened in Paris	
summer	trip to Barcelona and Madrid	
1918	Paul Rosenberg became Picasso's dealer	
July 12	married Olga Koklova	
summer	trip to Barcelona, stay in Biarritz where he decorated rooms in the villa of Mme Errazuriz	
October	moved to 23 rue La Boëtie, Paris	
November 9	Apollinaire, one of his closest friends, died	
1919 early	went to London with the Ballet Russe; made designs for *Le Tricorne*	
summer	Saint-Raphael (Côte d'Azur)	
summer	met Joan Miró	
1920 May 15	first performance of *Pulcinella* in Paris with Picasso's designs	
summer	Juan-les-Pins	

1921	February 4	son Paul was born
	May 22	first performance of *Cuadro flamenco* in Paris with his designs
	summer	Fontainebleau
		painted the two versions of the *Three Musicians*, one in The Philadelphia Museum of Art, the other in The Museum of Modern Art, New York
1922	summer	Dinard (Britanny)
	December 20	first performance of Cocteau's *Antigone*
1923	summer	Cap d'Antibes
1924	June 14	first performance in Paris of *Mercure* with Picasso's designs
	June 20	first performance of *Le Train Bleu* with his curtain
	summer	Juan-les-Pins
1925	spring	Monte Carlo
	summer	Juan-les-Pins
		participated in first exhibition of Surrealist painting in Paris at the Galerie Pierre
1926	summer	Juan-les-Pins
1927	summer	Cannes
1928	summer	Dinard
		began to work at sculpture again
1929	summer	Dinard
1930	summer	Juan-les-Pins
		bought Château de Boisgeloup, Gisors (Eure)
1931		Vollard published Balzac's *Le chef d'oeuvre inconnu* with illustrations by Picasso; Skira published Ovid's *Metamorphoses* with his illustrations
	summer	Juan-les-Pins
		began to work on welded sculpture with his friend, the Spanish sculptor Gonzalez, at Boisgeloup
1932		attachment began to Marie-Thérèse Walter
1933	spring	began etchings of the *Sculptor's Studio*
		trip to Cannes and Barcelona
1934		lived at Boisgeloup and Cannes; trip to Spain
		publication of Aristophanes' *Lysistrata* with illustrations by Picasso

1935		separated from Olga Koklova
	spring	etched the *Minotaurmachie*
		birth of daughter Maïa by Marie-Thérèse
1936	March 27 to May 14	Juan-les-Pins
	August	Côte d'Azur
	August 14 to mid-September	Mougins
		Dora Maar began to live with Picasso
		Picasso was named the Director of the Prado after the outbreak of the Spanish Civil War
		rented a house in Le Tremblay-sur-Mauldre from Vollard (until 1939)
1937		published the *Dream and Lie of General Franco*
	April 28	Spanish town of Guernica was wiped out by German bombers
	May 1	Picasso began to work on studies for his painting *Guernica*
	June	The *Guernica* was exhibited in the Spanish pavilion at the Paris World's Fair
	summer	Mougins
	autumn	short trip to Switzerland, met Paul Klee
1938	summer	Mougins and Le Tremblay
1939		Mother died in Barcelona
	summer	Antibes
	September 4	Royan
1940		Royan with trips to Paris
	August 24	returns to Paris until the end of the occupation
1941		wrote the play *Le desir attrapé par la queue (Desire Caught by the Tail)*
1942		after the Liberation participated in his first official exhibition in France, the Salon d'Automne
		joined the French Communist party
1945	summer	Golfe Juan and Menerbes where he bought a house for Dora Maar
		painted the *Charnel House*, the Chrysler Collection
	November 2	took up lithography in workshop of Fernand Mourlot

1946		Françoise Gillot began to live with Picasso
	summer	Golfe Juan
	autumn	Antibes where he gave recent works to Musée Grimaldi
1947		son Claude was born
	August	Golfe Juan, then Vallauris
		took up ceramics with the Madoura pottery at Vallauris
1948		settled in Vallauris at the villa La Galloise
	August	went to the first Communist sponsored Peace Congress in Poland
1949		birth of daughter Paloma
1950		exhibition at the Venice Biennale
	November	attended third Peace Congress in Sheffield, England
		named honourary citizen of Vallauris
1951		attended fourth Peace Congress in Rome, visited Sistine Chapel and on way home Arezzo and Assisi
		lived in Paris briefly at 9 rue Gay-Lussac
1952		painted *War and Peace*
1953	summer	Françoise Gillot left Picasso
1954		Jacqueline Roque began to live with Picasso
		summer in Collioure and Perpignan
		painted the series based upon Delacroix's *Femmes d'Alger*
1955	winter	Paris
		his wife, Olga Koklova Picasso, died in Cannes
		moved to new villa, la Californie, at Cannes
1957	August	Picasso devoted himself to his variations on Velazquez's *las Meninas*
1958	March 2	married Jacqueline Roque
	autumn	bought Château de Vauvenargues near Aix-en-Provence
1960	October	bought Mas Nôtre-Dame-de-Vie at Mougins
1961		painted series based on Manet's *Déjeuner sur l'herbe*
	June 14	moved to Nôtre-Dame-de-Vie

LIST OF ABBREVIATIONS

OTHER THAN EXHIBITIONS

Arts Council: The Arts Council of Great Britain, *Picasso: Fifty Years of Graphic Art* (Catalogue), London, June 22 to August 5, 1956.

Barr: Alfred H. Barr, *Picasso, Fifty Years of His Art,* New York: The Museum of Modern Art, 1946.

Blunt & Pool: Anthony Blunt and Phoebe Pool, *Picasso, the Formative Years,* London: Studio, 1962.

Boeck & Sabartés: Wilhelm Boeck and Jaime Sabartés, *Picasso,* New York: Abrams, 1961.

Bolliger: Hans Bolliger, *Picasso's Vollard Suite,* London: Thames and Hudson, 1956.

Cooper: Douglas Cooper, *Picasso: Les Déjeuners,* New York: Abrams, 1963.

Duncan: David D. Duncan, *Picasso's Picassos,* London: MacMillan, 1961.

G: Bernhard Geiser, *Picasso, Peintre-Graveur, catalogue illustré de l'oeuvre gravé et lithographié, 1899-1931,* vol. I, Berne: published by the author, 1933 and 1955.

Jardot: Maurice Jardot, *Picasso Drawings,* London: Thames and Hudson, 1959.

M: Fernand Mourlot, *Picasso Lithographe,* 3 vol., Monte Carlo: Andre Sauret, 1949-56.

Merli: Joan Merli, *Picasso, el artista y la obra de nuestro tiempo,* Buenos Aires: El Ateneo, 1942.

Millier: Arthur Millier, *The Drawings of Picasso,* Los Angeles: Borden, 1961.

Olivier: Fernande Olivier, *Picasso et ses Amis,* Paris: Stock, 1933.

Penrose: Roland Penrose, *Picasso: His Life and Work,* New York: Harper, 1959.

Rosenblum: Robert Rosenblum, *Cubism and Twentieth-Century Art,* New York: Abrams, 1960.

Stein: Gertrude Stein, *Picasso,* Boston: Beacon Press, 1959.

Vallentin: Antonina Vallentin, *Pablo Picasso,* Paris: Albin Michel, 1957.

Z: Christian Zervos, *Picasso, Oeuvre Catalogue,* 12 vol., Paris: Cahiers d'Art, 1932-61.

EXHIBITIONS

Boston 1938: *Picasso; Henri-Matisse,* Museum of Modern Art, October 19 to November 11.

Boston 1940: See New York 1939, MMA. Museum of Fine Arts (under auspices of Institute of Fine Arts), April 26 to May 25 (236 out of original 344 items).

Boston 1959: *Picasso from 1907 to 1909,* Museum of Fine Arts, March 15 to April 15.

Bremen 1961: *Picasso,* Kunsthalle, June 23 to August 6.

Brussels 1946: *27 Oeuvres de Pablo Picasso (1939-1945),* Palais des Beaux-Arts, May. Preface by Christian Zervos.

Chicago 1940: See New York 1939, MMA. The Art Institute of Chicago, February 1 to March 3 (236 out of original 344 items).

Chicago 1957: See New York 1957, MMA. *Picasso: 75th Anniversary Exhibition,* The Art Institute of Chicago, October 29 to December 8.

Cincinnati 1940: See New York 1940, MMA. Cincinnati Museum of Art (under auspices of Cincinnati Modern Art Society) September 28 to October 27 (170 items out of original 344 items).

Cleveland 1940: See New York 1940, MMA. Cleveland Museum of Art, November 7 to December 8 (170 out of original 344 items).

Cologne 1956: See Münich 1955. Rheinisches Museum, December 30, 1955 to February 29.

Denver 1945: *Paintings, Sculpture and Drawings by Picasso,* Art Museum, April 12 to May 12, mimeographed list; no catalogue numbers.

Dresden 1914: *Picasso,* Emil Richter Gallery.

Hamburg 1956: See Münich 1955. Kunsthalle, March 10 to April 29.

Hartford 1934: *Pablo Picasso,* Wadsworth Atheneum, February 6 to March 1.

Houston 1955: *Picasso Exhibit,* Contemporary Arts Museum, January 14 to February 20.

London 1939: *Picasso in English Collections,* the London Gallery, May.

London 1953, Lefevre: *Picasso (1898-1936),* Lefevre Gallery, May 1 to June 30.

London 1954, Lefevre: *Picasso (1938-53),* Lefevre Gallery, May.

London 1960, Arts Council: *Picasso,* The Arts Council of Great Britain, The Tate Gallery, July 6 to September 18. Catalogue by Roland Penrose.

Los Angeles 1961, UCLA: *Bonne Fête M. Picasso,* October 25 to November 12.

Lucerne, 1961, Rosengart: *Picasso Gemalde 1950-60,* Galerie Rosengart, summer. No catalogue numbers.

Lucerne, 1963, Rosengart: *Picasso: Deux Epoques,* Galerie Rosengart, summer. No catalogue numbers.

Lyon 1953: *Picasso,* Musée de Lyon.

Madrid 1936: *Picasso,* Amigos de las Artes Nuevas. Text by Guillermo de Torre.

Marseille 1959: *Picasso,* Musée Cantini, May 11 to July 31. Catalogue by Douglas Cooper.

Mexico 1944: *Picasso,* Sociedad de Arte Moderno, June.

Milan 1953: *Pablo Picasso,* Palazzo Reale, September to November.

Minneapolis 1941: See New York 1941, MMA. Minneapolis Institute of Arts, February 1 to March 2 (170 out of original 344 items).

Münich 1923, Thannhauser: *Austellung Pablo Picasso (1906-13),* Moderne Galerie.

Münich 1955: *Picasso,* Haus der Kunst, October 25 to December 26.

New Orleans 1940-41: See New York 1940, MMA. Isaac Delgado Museum (under sponsorship of Picasso Exhibition Committee), December 20 to January 17 (170 out of original 344 items).

New York 1930, Reinhardt: *Picasso and Derain,* Reinhardt Galleries, January 25 to February 21. Introduction by J. J. Sweeney.

New York 1936, Seligmann: *Picasso: 'Blue' and 'Rose' Periods, 1901-06,* Jacques Seligmann & Co., Inc., November 2 to November 26.

New York 1936, Valentine: *Retrospective Exhibition 1901-1934 Picasso,* Valentine Galleries, October 26 to November 21.

New York 1937, Seligmann: *Twenty Years in the Evolution of Picasso, 1903-23,* Jacques Seligmann & Co., Inc., November 1 to November 20.

New York 1938, Valentine: *Picasso: Twenty-one Paintings–1908-1934,* Valentine Gallery, November 7 to November 26.

New York 1939, MMA: *Picasso, Forty Years of his Art,* The Museum of Modern Art, November 15, 1939 to January 7. Catalogue by Alfred Barr.

New York 1941-42, MMA: *Picasso: Epochs in his Art,* an exhibition circulated by The Museum of Modern Art to Utica, Durham, Kansas City, Milwaukee, Grand Rapids, Hanover, Poughkeepsie. See Barr p. 279 for dates.

New York 1945, Buchholz: *Picasso,* Buchholz Gallery, February 27 to March 17.

New York 1947, Knoedler: *Picasso Before 1907,* Knoedler Galleries, October 15 to November 8.

New York 1947, Kootz: *Picasso,* Kootz Gallery, from August 25.

New York 1948, Kootz: *Picasso,* Kootz Gallery, January 26 to February 14.

New York 1948, Rosenberg: *Drawings, Gouaches, Paintings from 1913 to 1947 by Pablo Picasso,* Paul Rosenberg, New York, March 16 to April 3.

New York 1952, Valentin: *Pablo Picasso–Paintings, Sculpture, Drawings,* Curt Valentin Gallery, February 19 to March 15.

New York 1953, Perls: *Picasso: The Thirties,* Perls Galleries, January 5 to February 7.

New York 1953, Valentin: *Pablo Picasso, 1950-53,* Curt Valentin Gallery, November 24 to December 19.

New York 1955, MMA: *Picasso: 12 Masterworks,* The Museum of Modern Art, March 15 to April 24.

New York 1956, Chalette: *Picasso: 'The Woman,'* Galerie Chalette, April 16 to May 19.

New York 1956, Kootz: *Picasso,* Kootz Gallery, March 12 to April 7. No catalogue numbers.

New York 1957, MMA: *Picasso: 75th Anniversary Exhibition,* The Museum of Modern Art, May 22 to September 8.

New York 1959, Saidenberg: *Picasso, Faces and Figures, 1900 to 1959,* Saidenberg Gallery, November 10 to December 12.

New York 1962, Kootz: *Picasso,* Kootz Gallery, October 2 to October 20.

New York 1962, MMA: *Picasso in The Museum of Modern Art: 80th Birthday Exhibition,* The Museum of Modern Art, May 15 to September 18, mimeographed list. No exhibition numbers.

New York 1962, Tribute: *Picasso: An American Tribute,* M. Knoedler and Co., Inc., Saidenberg Gallery, Paul Rosenberg and Co., Duveen Brothers, Inc., Perls Galleries, Staempfli Gallery, Inc., Cordier-Warren Gallery, The New Gallery, Otto Gerson Gallery, April 25 to May 12. Catalogue by John Richardson.

Oslo 1955: *Pablo Picasso,* Kunstnernes Hus, November 1 to December 31.

Paris 1902: *Exposition de Peintures, Pastels et Dessins par MM. Girieud, Launay, Picasso et Pichot,* Galerie B. Weill, November 15 to December 15.

Paris 1932: *Exposition Picasso,* Galeries Georges Petit, June 16 to July 30.

Paris 1936, Rosenberg: *Exposition d'Oeuvres Récentes de Picasso,* Galerie Paul Rosenberg, March 3 to March 31.

Paris 1946, Carré: *Dix-Neuf Peintures de Picasso,* Galerie Louis Carré, June 14 to July 14.

Paris 1954, la Pensée française I: *Picasso oeuvres des musées de Leningrad et de Moscou, 1900-14,* Maison de la Pensée française, June.

Paris 1954, la Pensée française II: *Picasso: deux periodes; 1900-14, 1950-54,* Maison de la Pensée française, n.d.

Paris 1955, Décoratifs: *Picasso,* Musée des Arts Décoratifs, June to October. Catalogue by Maurice Jardot.

Paris 1957, Leiris: *Picasso: Peintures 1955-1956,* Galerie Louise Leiris, March to April.

Paris 1962, Leiris: *Picasso: Peintures (Vauvenargues 1959-1961),* Galerie Louise Leiris, January 26 to February 24.

Paris 1962, Leiris, Déjeuner: *Picasso: Le Déjeuner sur l'Herbe 1960-1961,* Galerie Louise Leiris, June 6 to July 13.

Philadelphia 1958: *Picasso: A Loan Exhibition of His Paintings, Drawings, Sculptures, Ceramics, Prints and Illustrated Books,* Philadelphia Museum of Art, January 8 to February 23.

Pittsburgh 1941: See New York 1939, MMA. Carnegie Institute, March 15 to April 13 (170 out of original 344 items).

Princeton 1949: *Picasso Drawings,* The Art Museum, Princeton University, January 10 to January 31.

Rome 1953: *Pablo Picasso,* Galleria Nazionale.

Saint Louis 1940: See New York 1939, MMA. City Art Museum of St. Louis, March 16 to April 14 (236 out of original 344 items).

San Antonio 1954: *Picasso,* Inaugural Exhibition, Marian Koogler McNay Art Institute, November 4 to December 5.

San Francisco 1940: See New York 1939, MMA. San Francisco Museum of Art, April 26 to May 25 (236 out of original 344 items).

Santa Barbara 1960: *Picasso,* Santa Barbara Museum of Art, January 15 to February 7.

São Paulo 1954: *Exposicao Picasso,* Museu de Arte Modern de São Paulo, December 1953 to February. Catalogue by Maurice Jardot.

Toronto 1949: *Picasso,* The Art Gallery of Toronto, April.

Worcester 1962: *Picasso–His Later Works 1938-1961,* Worcester Art Museum, January 25 to February 25. Catalogue by Daniel Catton Rich.

Zürich 1932: *Picasso,* Kunsthaus, September 11 to October 30.

SELECTED BIBLIOGRAPHY

GENERAL BOOKS

Alfred H. Barr, *Picasso, Fifty Years of his Art*, New York: The Museum of Modern Art, 1946.

Wilhelm Boeck and Jaime Sabartés, *Picasso*, London: Thames & Hudson; New York: Abrams, 1955.

BIBLIOGRAPHICAL REVIEW

(Douglas Cooper), "Pablo Picasso, the Artist as Subject," *The Times Literary Supplement*, no. 3,121, Friday, December 22, 1961.

BACKGROUND

Guillaume Apollinaire, *The Cubist Painters*, tr. by L. Abel, New York: Wittenborn, 1944.

Christopher Gray, *Cubist Aesthetic Theories*, Baltimore: Johns Hopkins, 1953.

D.-H. Kahnweiler, *The Rise of Cubism*, New York: Wittenborn, 1949.

John Golding, *Cubism*, London: Faber, 1959.

J. F. Ráfols, *Modernism y Modernistas*, Barcelona: Destino, 1949.

Robert Rosenblum, *Cubism and Twentieth Century Art*, New York: Abrams, 1960.

REMINISCENCES OF PICASSO

David D. Duncan, *The Private World of Pablo Picasso*, New York: Ridge Press, 1958.

D.-H. Kahnweiler, *Entretiens*, Paris: Gallimard, 1961.

Fernande Olivier, *Picasso et ses Amis*, Paris: Stock, 1933.

Hélène Parmelin, *Picasso sur la Place*, Paris: Juillard, 1959.

Hélène Parmelin, *Picasso Plain*, tr. by H. Hare, London: Secker & Warburg, 1963.

Jaime Sabartés, *Picasso, Portraits et Souvenirs*, Paris: Louis Carré et Maximilien Vox, 1946.

André Salmon, *Souvenirs sans Fin*, 2 vols., Paris: Gallimard, 1955-56.

BIOGRAPHIES OF PICASSO

Roland Penrose, *Picasso: His Life and Work*, London: Gollancz, 1958.

Roland Penrose, *Portrait of Picasso*, London: Lund Humphries, 1956.

Jaime Sabartés, *Picasso, Documents Iconographiques*, Geneva: Cailler, 1954.

Antonina Vallentin, *Pablo Picasso*, Paris: Albin Michel, 1957.

CRITICISM OF PICASSO'S WORK

Guillaume Apollinaire, *Chroniques d'Art*, Paris: Gallimard, 1960.

Pierre de Champris, *Picasso, Ombre et Soleil*, Paris: Gallimard, 1960.

Gertrude Stein, *Picasso*, London: Batsford, 1938.

CATALOGUES OF PICASSO'S WORK

Christian Zervos, *Picasso, Oeuvre Catalogue*, 12 vols., Paris: Cahiers d'Art, 1932-61.

David D. Duncan, *Picasso's Picassos*, London: Macmillan, 1961.

Maurice Jardot, *Picasso Drawings*, London: Thames & Hudson; New York: Abrams, 1959.

D.-H. Kahnweiler, *Les Sculptures de Picasso*, Paris: Editions du Chêne, 1949.

Bernard Geiser, *Picasso, Fifty-five Years of his Graphic Work*, London: Thames & Hudson, 1955; New York: Abrams, 1955.

Bernard Geiser, *Picasso, Peintre Graveur, catalogue illustré de l'oeuvre gravé et lithographié, 1899-1931*, vol. I, Berne: author, 1933 and 1955.

Fernand Mourlot, *Picasso Lithographe*, 3 vols., Monte Carlo: André Sauret, 1949-56.

STUDIES OF PERIODS OR WORKS

Sir Anthony Blunt and Phoebe Pool, *Picasso, the Formative Years*, London: Studio, 1962.

A. Cirici-Pellicer, *Picasso avant Picasso*, Geneva: Pierre Cailler, 1950.

Harriet and Sidney Janis, *Picasso: the Recent Years, 1939-46*, New York: Doubleday, 1946.

Douglas Cooper (ed.), *Picasso: Carnet Catalan*, Paris: Berggruen, 1958.

Rudolph Arnheim, *Picasso's Guernica*, Berkeley: University of California Press, 1962.

Juan Larrea (ed.), *Guernica*, New York: Curt Valentin, 1947.

Claude Roy (ed.), *La Guerre et la Paix*, Paris: Editions Cercle d'Art, 1952.

Jaime Sabartés, *Les Ménines*, Paris: Editions Cercle d'Art, *Picasso's Variations on Velazquez' Painting 'Maids of Honour'*, London: Thames & Hudson, 1958.

Georges Boudaille (ed.), *Picasso, Carnet de la Californie*, Paris: Editions Cercle d'Art, 1959.

Luis Miguel Dominguin & Georges Boudaille (ed.), *Toro y Toreros*, Paris: Editions Cercle d'Art, 1961.

Douglas Cooper, *Picasso: les Déjeuners*, Paris: Editions Cercle d'Art, 1962.

CREDITS

Production editor and designer
FRANK NEWFELD

Printer
MIRROR OFFSET COMPANY

Typographer
LINOTYPE COMPOSING CO LTD

Typeface
OPTIMA

Papers
TEXOPAKE & LOUVAIN